Trade up to a higher grade with CGP!

GCSE Business isn't easy, but you don't need to go it alone... this fantastic CGP book is the perfect partner for your revision!

It's bursting with realistic exam-style questions on everything from production to procurement — including the context-based questions that are a big part of the Grade 9-1 exams.

We've also put answers to every question at the back of the book, so once you've done the work, it's easy to ~~market~~ mark it.

CGP — still the best! ☺

Our sole aim here at CGP is to produce the highest quality books — carefully written, immaculately presented and dangerously close to being funny.

Then we work our socks off to get them out to you — at the cheapest possible prices.

Published by CGP

Editors:
Charlotte Burrows, Emily Howe, Ciara McGlade and Rachael Rogers

With thanks to Glenn Rogers and Victoria Skelton for the proofreading.

With thanks to Ana Pungartnik for the copyright research.

ISBN: 978 1 78294 692 2

Clipart from Corel®
Printed by Elanders Ltd, Newcastle upon Tyne

Based on the classic CGP style created by Richard Parsons.

Contents

Use the tick boxes to check off the topics you've completed.

How to Use This Book

- Hold the book upright, approximately 50 cm from your face, ensuring that the text looks like this, not sıɥʇ. Alternatively, place the book on a horizontal surface (e.g. a table or desk) and sit adjacent to the book, at a distance which doesn't make the text too small to read.
- In case of emergency, press the two halves of the book together firmly in order to close.
- Before attempting to use this book, familiarise yourself with the following safety information:

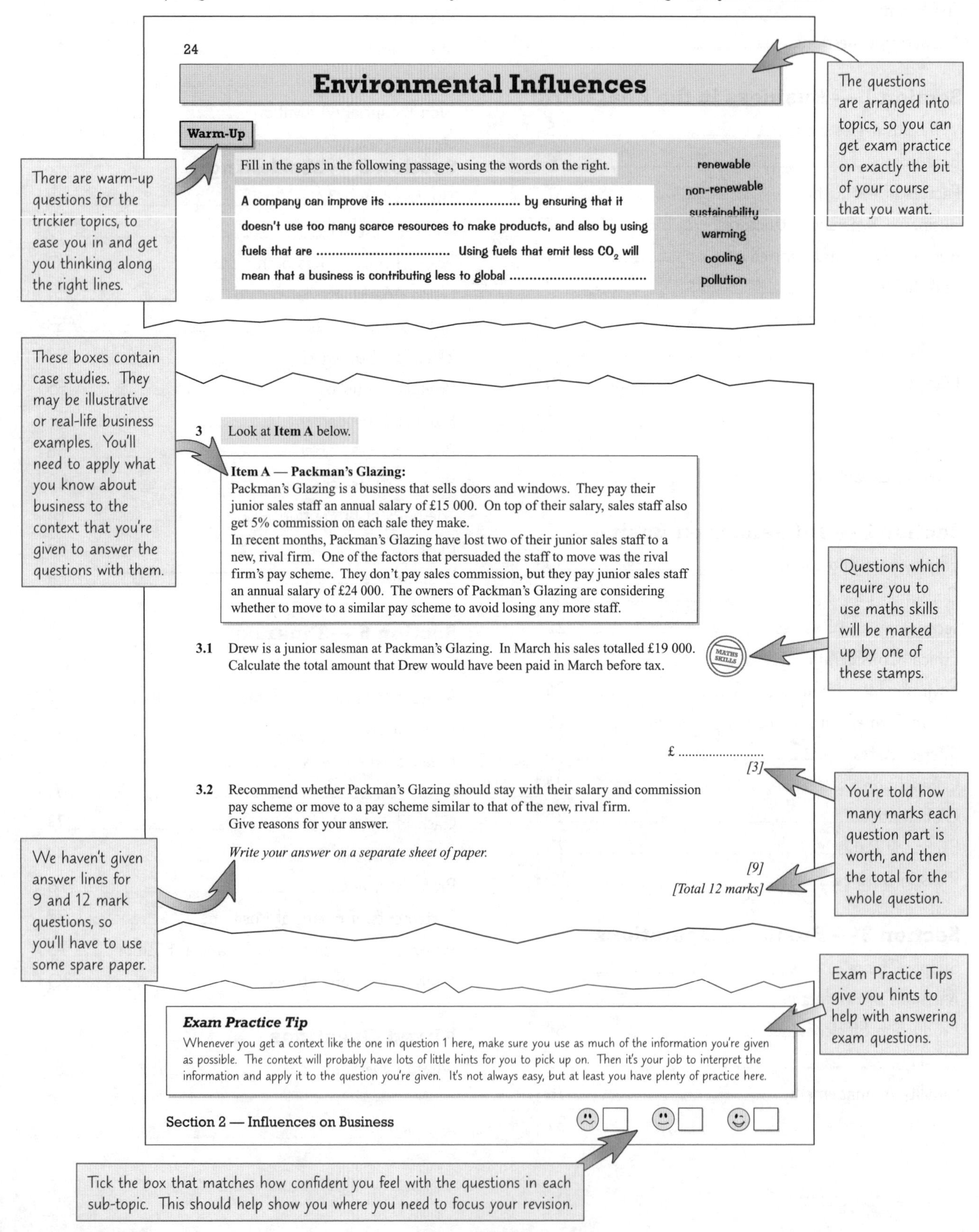

24

Environmental Influences

The questions are arranged into topics, so you can get exam practice on exactly the bit of your course that you want.

Warm-Up

There are warm-up questions for the trickier topics, to ease you in and get you thinking along the right lines.

Fill in the gaps in the following passage, using the words on the right.

A company can improve its .... by ensuring that it doesn't use too many scarce resources to make products, and also by using fuels that are .... Using fuels that emit less CO_2 will mean that a business is contributing less to global ....

renewable
non-renewable
sustainability
warming
cooling
pollution

These boxes contain case studies. They may be illustrative or real-life business examples. You'll need to apply what you know about business to the context that you're given to answer the questions with them.

3 Look at **Item A** below.

Item A — Packman's Glazing:
Packman's Glazing is a business that sells doors and windows. They pay their junior sales staff an annual salary of £15 000. On top of their salary, sales staff also get 5% commission on each sale they make.
In recent months, Packman's Glazing have lost two of their junior sales staff to a new, rival firm. One of the factors that persuaded the staff to move was the rival firm's pay scheme. They don't pay sales commission, but they pay junior sales staff an annual salary of £24 000. The owners of Packman's Glazing are considering whether to move to a similar pay scheme to avoid losing any more staff.

3.1 Drew is a junior salesman at Packman's Glazing. In March his sales totalled £19 000. Calculate the total amount that Drew would have been paid in March before tax.

MATHS SKILLS

Questions which require you to use maths skills will be marked up by one of these stamps.

£ ....
[3]

You're told how many marks each question part is worth, and then the total for the whole question.

3.2 Recommend whether Packman's Glazing should stay with their salary and commission pay scheme or move to a pay scheme similar to that of the new, rival firm.
Give reasons for your answer.

Write your answer on a separate sheet of paper.

[9]
[Total 12 marks]

We haven't given answer lines for 9 and 12 mark questions, so you'll have to use some spare paper.

Exam Practice Tips give you hints to help with answering exam questions.

Exam Practice Tip
Whenever you get a context like the one in question 1 here, make sure you use as much of the information you're given as possible. The context will probably have lots of little hints for you to pick up on. Then it's your job to interpret the information and apply it to the question you're given. It's not always easy, but at least you have plenty of practice here.

Section 2 — Influences on Business

Tick the box that matches how confident you feel with the questions in each sub-topic. This should help show you where you need to focus your revision.

The Exams

These two pages have some information and tips on what to expect in the exams, to help you do really well. You might find it useful to read through them before answering any questions, then you can put what you've read into practice.

There Are Two Exam Papers — Paper 1 and Paper 2

Paper 1

- Paper 1 is 1 hour and 45 minutes long.
- It's worth 90 marks and is 50% of your total Business GCSE.
- It'll test you on the topics in Sections 1, 2, 3 and 4 of this book.

Paper 2

- Paper 2 is 1 hour and 45 minutes long.
- It's worth 90 marks and is 50% of your total Business GCSE.
- It'll test you on the topics in Sections 1, 2, 5 and 6 of this book.

1) In both papers there'll be three sections.
2) Section A is a mixture of multiple choice and short answer questions, and is worth 20 marks.
3) Sections B and C are both based around a case study, which could include some data. You'll have to answer a mixture of short and long questions related to the information in each case study.

There are lots of questions that are based on case studies throughout this book. These case studies may be illustrative examples, or real-life businesses. Don't worry that you don't know the details of each case study — the trick is to apply what you know about business in general to each situation.

The Examiners are Looking for Three Types of Skills

There are basically three types of skill and knowledge that you need to show to get marks in the exams:

Demonstrate knowledge and understanding

- This skill is about recalling, selecting and communicating.
- You need to show that you've got a really good understanding of the facts, and that you can use appropriate business terms, e.g. sole trader, marketing mix, supply chain.

Apply knowledge and understanding

- This skill is all about applying what you know to different situations.
- Make sure your answer is relevant to the situation that's been described.
- For example, an exam question might tell you about a sole trader who wants to buy a new piece of equipment, and ask you to suggest how they could raise the necessary finance. Here, you wouldn't want to suggest that the company issue more shares (since only a limited company can have shares and sole traders are unlimited).

Analyse and evaluate to demonstrate understanding, make judgements and draw conclusions

- This skill is all about using evidence to make judgements and reach conclusions.
- For example, if you recommend that a business raise money using a mortgage rather than an overdraft, you need to explain why, using what you know about finance.
- Your ideas need to be structured in a logical way so that your arguments make sense.
- Often, these questions won't have a right answer. The important thing is using evidence from the question to support the conclusion you've come to.

Exam Practice Tip

So there are two exams and each is 1 hour and 45 minutes long. Remember the different skills the examiners will be looking for — knowing what they want can help you predict what to write for answers, and make your life a bit easier.

Answering Questions

Here's some information on the different types of questions you can get, and how you should answer each one.

Make Sure you Read the Question

1) Command words are just the bit of the question that tell you what to do.
2) Here's a summary of the most common command words, so you know what to do with them in the exams:

Command word	What to do
State or identify	These words ask for a statement — you don't need to back it up with evidence.
Explain	This means you need to give reasons for things. You need to show that you understand the connection between things that happen in the world and the effects they have on businesses.
Analyse	This means "Examine in detail." You should talk about the main features of the thing you're analysing. Then explain how or why these features work together to lead to the end result.
Calculate	Some questions ask for a bit of maths. Remember to show your working.
Complete	You need to fill in the missing parts of some information you've been given (e.g. complete a table).
Recommend	You'll be given some information about a business and asked to say whether the business should do something, or to choose between two options for what the business could do.
Evaluate	You should discuss both sides of an issue. You should finish your answer with a conclusion giving an overall judgement.
Give reasons for your answer	This means you need to include lots of points and explain why they're relevant to your answer. Link your ideas together to build a balanced argument.
Use evidence to support your answer	This means you need to pick out specific information from a case study or piece of data that you've been given, in order to back up your answer.

3) In general, you'll need to spend more time and write more for questions that are worth more marks.
4) Questions asking you to analyse a situation or recommend a decision for a business to make are worth the most — they'll be 6, 9 or 12 marks. For these questions, it might help to write a quick plan to make sure you don't miss anything, and to make sure you show all the skills from the previous page.

You'll have to Answer Questions About Case Studies

1) For questions that are based on case study information or on data, make sure you use evidence from the case study or data set as well as your knowledge of Business in your answer.
2) For questions using 'analyse' or 'recommend' command words, there will usually be advantages and disadvantages of a situation to think about — to get all the marks, you'll need to give both sides of the argument before coming to a conclusion.
3) Before you get started on your answer, read the case study and any data all the way through. Then read the whole question carefully and make sure you've understood what you're being asked to do.

You'll be Tested on Your Maths Skills

1) In your exams, you'll have to do some maths — e.g. do some calculations using financial data, or interpret a graph.
2) For calculation questions, always make sure you show your working — even if your final answer's wrong, you could still get some marks if your method was correct.
3) And don't forget to take a calculator to the exams.

In this book, questions that test your maths skills are shown by this stamp: MATHS SKILLS

Exam Practice Tip

For each question in the exam, look at the command words and the number of marks. Remember that longer questions are usually testing your judgement as well as your knowledge, so you should support your ideas with evidence.

Why Businesses Exist

Warm-Up

Place the businesses on the left into correct column of the table, depending on whether they mainly sell goods or services.

taxi firm greengrocers

dentist furniture shop

online clothes store

cinema accountancy firm

Goods	Services

1 Andzelika has a small business that makes greetings cards.
Which of the following explains the purpose of Andzelika's business?
Shade **one** oval only.

A To produce goods. ⬭

B To distribute products. ⬭

C To provide a need. ⬭

D To provide a service to benefit others. ⬭

[Total 1 mark]

2 Explain, using **one** example of each, the difference between needs and wants.

....

....

....

....

[Total 4 marks]

3 Peter owns a dairy farm. He uses some of the milk from his farm to make luxury ice cream. Explain how Peter's farm is part of **two** sectors of the economy.

....

....

....

....

....

[Total 4 marks]

Enterprise

1 Which of the following statements describes what is meant by the term 'enterprise'? Shade **one** oval only.

- **A** Managing a successful company. ⬭
- **B** Identifying and taking advantage of new business opportunities. ⬭
- **C** Running a business without any help from others. ⬭
- **D** Taking risks in business. ⬭

[Total 1 mark]

2 Look at **Item A** below.

> **Item A — Harte & Sole:**
> In 2013, Bushra Ahmed realised there weren't any companies that produced fashionable, vegan-friendly and ethically produced shoes, and that people would be willing to buy them. So she quit a high-pressure job as a journalist to set up her ethical shoe company, Harte & Sole. After visiting many trade shows, she found a manufacturer who could provide her with the shoes she needed, in small quantities so she never needed to hold much stock at her small office. In 2014, Bushra was invited to pitch her shoes to a nationwide retail chain. In the two weeks before her presentation, Bushra worked every day to prepare herself. The pitch was a success and the retail chain gave Bushra a contract to supply them with her shoes.

2.1 Explain **one** reason why Bushra may have wanted to start her own business.

....

....

[2]

2.2 Explain why the word 'entrepreneur' can be used to describe Bushra.

....

....

[2]

2.3 Analyse how Bushra has shown that she has the qualities needed to be a successful entrepreneur.

....

....

....

....

....

....

....

....

[6]

[Total 10 marks]

Factors of Production

1 Explain what is meant by the following factors of production, and give **one** example of each.

Land: ....

....

Capital: ....

....

[Total 4 marks]

2 Look at **Item A** below.

> **Item A — Special Day Bouquet:**
> Dirk owns Special Day Bouquet, a florist shop that provides unique bouquets for events and weddings. Dirk is the only person in the business who is able to make these bouquets. One weekend he is offered two contracts. The first is to provide bouquets and table decorations for a photo shoot for a wedding magazine. For this he would receive £600 and have his business's name printed in the magazine. The second is to provide flowers for a local stately home that is holding an art festival, for which he would receive £1000. Dirk doesn't have enough time to prepare flowers for both events, so decides to accept the offer from the stately home.

2.1 Explain which factor of production is limiting Dirk's ability to take on both contracts.

....

....

....

[2]

2.2 Use the information in **Item A** to explain the term 'opportunity cost'.

....

....

....

....

....

[3]

[Total 5 marks]

> ***Exam Practice Tip***
> Knowing your definitions is really important for business, and there are lots to learn in this section. Make sure you know the ins and outs of each definition so you can apply them to different contexts. Learning definitions may be about as interesting as watching paint dry, but it could help you pick up lots of marks in the exams.

Business Ownership Structures

Warm-Up

Draw circles to show whether the statements below are **true** or **false**.

1) Private limited companies can only sell new shares if all current shareholders agree. TRUE / FALSE
2) Partners generally have an equal share in a company. TRUE / FALSE
3) A public limited company is automatically formed when a private limited company has a certain number of shareholders. TRUE / FALSE
4) Sole trader businesses have shares that can be bought and sold by anybody. TRUE / FALSE

1 Which of the following is an advantage of being a sole trader? Shade **one** oval only.

A A sole trader has a partner to take care of running the business. ⬭

B It's easy and relatively cheap to start up as a sole trader. ⬭

C A sole trader can't lose more money than they've invested in the business. ⬭

D It's easy for the business to expand by making shares available for anyone to buy. ⬭

[Total 1 mark]

2 Explain **two** disadvantages of a sole trader business structure.

....

....

....

....

....

[Total 4 marks]

3 Explain why a private limited company is a good structure for a business where the owners want to have a lot of control but minimise their financial risks.

....

....

....

....

....

....

[Total 4 marks]

4 Explain **two** reasons why the owners of a partnership may be reluctant to change the business into a private limited company.

....

....

....

....

....

[Total 4 marks]

5 Look at **Item A** below.

Item A — The National Trust:
The National Trust is a not-for-profit business that preserves land and buildings in the UK.
The National Trust is an incorporated charity. Being a charity means that the National Trust is restricted in what it can sell, but it also means that it doesn't have to pay as much tax as non-charitable firms.
The National Trust raises money from donations and membership fees. It also owns some companies which aren't charities. These companies run things such as the National Trust shops. They donate their profits to the National Trust in a way that means the profits aren't taxed.

5.1 Explain what is meant by a 'not-for-profit business'.

....

....

....

[2]

5.2 Explain **one** advantage to the National Trust of owning separate companies that aren't charities.

....

....

....

....

[2]

5.3 Explain why being incorporated is beneficial to the people who run the National Trust.

....

....

....

....

[3]

[Total 7 marks]

6 Look at **Item B** below.

> **Item B — Blackwell's Pies Ltd.:**
> Blackwell's Pies Ltd. is a private limited company that was started 15 years ago by Keith Blackwell. The company makes pies for many of the leading supermarket chains. Currently, all the shares in the company are held by Mr. Blackwell and his family. The company has grown steadily since it was started and now the shareholders are considering becoming a public limited company.

Analyse the effect on the Blackwell family of making the business a public limited company.

[Total 6 marks]

7 Look at **Item C** below.

> **Item C — Accountancy Firm:**
> Kate has just qualified as an accountant and wants to open an accountancy firm. Although she has managed to get a bank loan, she doesn't have a lot of money to put into the business. Somebody she studied with has suggested that they start the business together, as a partnership. Kate doesn't know this person well, and is unsure whether they share her vision for the business.

7.1 Explain how a partnership works.

[3]

7.2 Recommend whether Kate should start her business as half of a partnership, or whether she should start up as a sole trader. Give reasons for your answer.
Write your answer on a separate piece of paper.

[9]

[Total 12 marks]

> ***Exam Practice Tip***
> The devil's in the detail where business ownership structures are concerned. Make sure you know the differences between sole traders, partnerships, Ltds. and PLCs, along with the advantages and disadvantages of each structure.

Business Aims and Objectives

1 Explain how business aims are different to business objectives.

....

....

....

[Total 3 marks]

2 Look at **Item A** below.

Item A — Karen's Sarnies:
Karen Booth is opening Karen's Sarnies, a small sandwich shop in Nantwich, Cheshire. In her first year, Karen's main aim is to survive. For the years after that, Karen has other aims, such as to maximise profit.

2.1 Identify **two** aims a small business might have, other than survival and maximising profit.

....

....

[2]

Item B — Karen's Sarnies:
Three years after Karen's Sarnies opened, Rye Ltd., a large, national sandwich retailer, opened a branch on the same street.

2.2 Explain **one** way in which the arrival of Rye Ltd. may have affected Karen's aims.

....

....

....

....

....

[4]

2.3 Explain why the aims for Rye Ltd. are likely to be different to the aims for Karen's Sarnies. Identify **one** aim Rye Ltd. might have in your answer.

....

....

....

....

[3]

[Total 9 marks]

3 Look at **Item C** and **Figure 1** below.

Item C — Merino:
At the start of 2008, Ole opened Merino, a business selling Scandinavian knitwear in the UK.
When he started the company, he set the following aims:
1. To make a profit within the first five years.
2. To have sales of over £1m per year by the fifth year.
3. To be a nationally recognised company after eight years.

For the first three years, Ole was selling his knitwear on the internet.
Then, in 2011, a retailer with three outlets in his local area started stocking his products.
In 2013, Ole put some adverts for his company in a national newspaper. This led to many more orders on his website, and in 2014 a national department store started stocking his products.

Figure 1

Yearly sales and profit for Merino, from 2008 to 2015

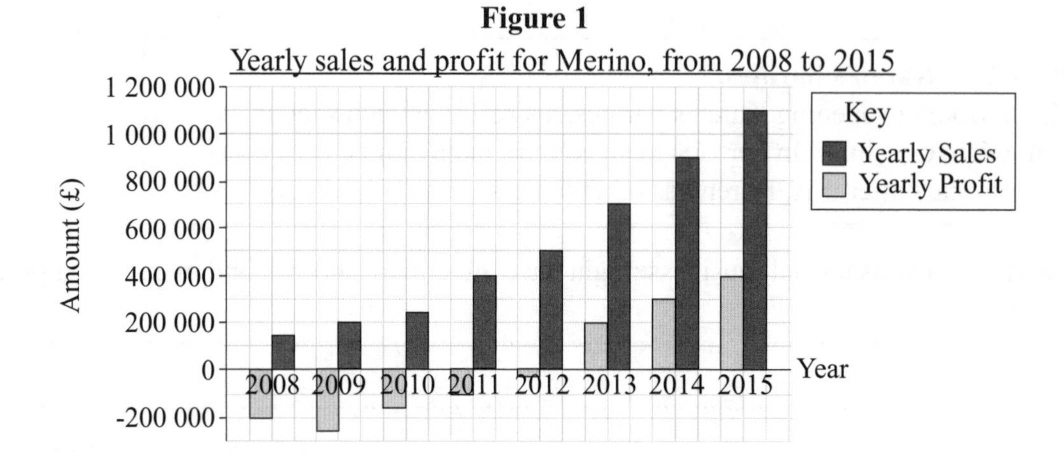

3.1 Explain how Ole could have used objectives to help him achieve his aim of sales of over £1m by the fifth year of starting the business.

....

....

....

[3]

3.2 Analyse the extent to which Ole was successful at achieving **two** of his aims. MATHS SKILLS

....

....

....

....

....

....

....

....

....

[6]

[Total 9 marks]

Stakeholders

1 Look at **Item A** below.

> **Item A — Better Energy Plc.:**
> Better Energy Plc. are a company that own power plants. In the last five years, their revenue has increased by 36% and profits have increased by 20%. As a result of this success, they have increased staff wages by 5% and cut the energy prices they charge customers by 3%. They have also invested in refurbishing their offices and have started investing in new power plants that generate electricity in a renewable way.

1.1 Explain **two** ways in which Better Energy Plc. may have satisfied the objectives of its customers.

....

....

....

....

....

....

[4]

> **Item B — Better Energy Plc.:**
> Better Energy Plc. are proposing to reinvest their profits and build a new wind farm. There are two sites they could use.
>
> The first site is near the town of Madingborough. As part of the project, Better Energy Plc. would also invest in improving the roads around Madingborough. Madingborough is in an Area of Outstanding Natural Beauty. Many of the local residents are employed in the local tourism industry. The residents have protested about the proposed wind farm, claiming that it will spoil the views of the area. The protests have attracted media attention and recently gained the support of minor celebrities.
>
> The second site is offshore. This option would cost double the price of the Madingborough site and take a year longer to build.

1.2 Analyse the impact that building a wind farm at Madingborough, rather than offshore, will have on the following stakeholders:

- the residents of Madingborough
- shareholders

You must evaluate which stakeholder's opinions will have the biggest impact on the business's final decision about where to build the wind farm. Use evidence to support your answer.
Write your answer on a separate piece of paper.

[12]

[Total 16 marks]

Revenue, Costs and Profit

Warm-Up

Circle the costs below that would be described as 'fixed costs' for a business.

raw materials | running machinery | insurance | wages for factory staff | rent | managers' salaries

1 Look at **Item A** and **Figure 1** below. 

> **Item A — Chow Mine:**
> Chow Mine are a company that produce and sell recipe kits. Between 2015 and 2016, their output increased from 10 000 to 12 500. Their costs and revenue in these years are shown in **Figure 1**.

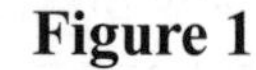

Figure 1

Costs and Revenue for Chow Mine in 2015 and 2016

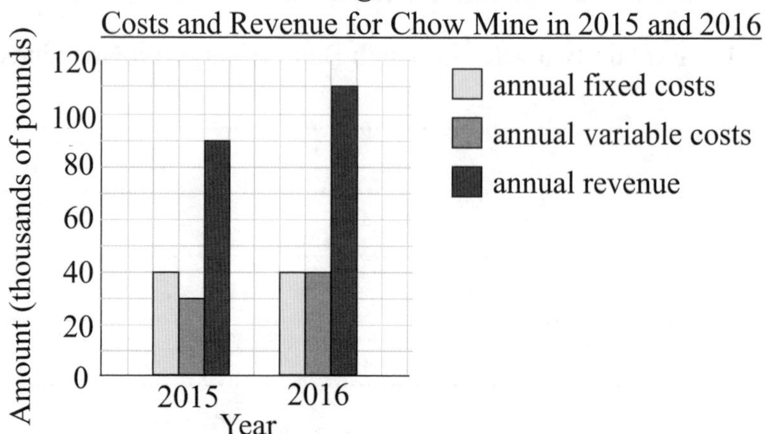

1.1 Explain what happened to costs between 2015 and 2016, as shown in **Figure 1**.

....

....

....

....

[4]

1.2 State the formula for calculating the average unit cost of a product, and calculate the average unit cost of one recipe kit in 2016.

Formula: ....

Average unit cost = £...........................

[3]

1.3 Calculate the percentage increase in profit between 2015 and 2016.

Percentage increase = ...%

[4]

[Total 11 marks]

The Business Plan

1 What is the purpose of the mission statement in a business plan?
Shade **one** oval only.

A To outline the broad aims of the company. ⬭

B To explain how the firm will achieve its unique selling point, and to give details of the market and competition. ⬭

C To describe what personnel the business will need. ⬭

D To explain how much money is needed to start up the business. ⬭

[Total 1 mark]

2 Look at **Item A** below.

Item A — Sam's Sweets:
Sam wants to start Sam's Sweets, a business manufacturing and selling flavoured marshmallows. Sam is hoping to get a loan from the bank to help start his business. He is going to write a business plan to take with him to the bank when he applies for his loan.

Before writing his business plan, Sam carries out some market research and finds there are no competitors in his area who sell flavoured marshmallows. Using this information, he predicts that his business will grow by 60% each year for the first five years. He also sets an aim of achieving a profit of £1m within seven years of opening.

2.1 Explain **one** reason why it is a good idea for Sam to write a business plan.

....

....

....

[2]

2.2 Explain **two** reasons why Sam's business plan may cause him problems in the future.

....

....

....

....

....

....

[4]

[Total 6 marks]

Location

1 Which of the following businesses is most likely to prioritise the location of the market when choosing where to locate? Shade **one** oval only.

A A company that sells stationery over the internet. ⬭

B A hairdresser. ⬭

C A courier service that delivers items nationally. ⬭

D A company that arranges package holidays over the phone. ⬭

[Total 1 mark]

2 Explain **one** reason why a UK business might choose to locate abroad.

....

....

....

[Total 2 marks]

3 Look at **Item A** below.

> **Item A — DP Oak Ltd.:**
> DP Oak Ltd. make flat-pack wardrobes which they sell over the internet.
> They want to expand their business by building a new factory. They are considering locating the factory near to Hampton, a large town with high levels of unemployment.

3.1 Explain **one** benefit of choosing to locate the new factory near to Hampton.

....

....

[2]

3.2 DP Oak Ltd. are considering two possible sites for the factory:

- **Site 1** is located on an industrial estate 10 miles from the town, and costs £2000 per month to rent. It is close to a wood-processing plant.
- **Site 2** is located close to the centre of town, and costs £3500 per month to rent. It is on a local bus route, and close to the local college as well as other, similar businesses.

Recommend which site would be better for the factory. Give reasons for your advice.
Write your answer on a separate piece of paper.

[9]

[Total 11 marks]

> ***Exam Practice Tip***
> The best location for a company largely depends on the type of business it is. If you get asked about the location of a particular business in the exam, think about things such as what it sells, who (and where) it sells to, the amount and type of labour it's likely to need, and the relative transport costs into and out of the site.

Expanding Businesses

1 Which of the following is the correct description of the term 'economy of scale'?
Shade **one** oval only.

A A reduction in corporation tax that a large business has to pay to the government. ⬭

B A reduction in total costs that results from operating a business on a larger scale. ⬭

C A reduction in average unit costs that results from operating a business on a larger scale. ⬭

D An increase in profits that results from businesses charging more for their products. ⬭

[Total 1 mark]

2 Look at **Item A** below.

> **Item A — VDP:**
> Anthony owns VDP — a company that provides call centre services to other firms.
> He recently expanded the business by building an extension to double the size of his call centre. He also hired 15 more staff members. In the first year after the expansion, Anthony found that the productivity of his staff fell by 20%. So after a year, he reorganised his business structure. Two years after the expansion, productivity was back to the point it had been before he expanded, and average weekly revenue had increased by 40%.

2.1 Explain how VDP experienced a diseconomy of scale and explain why this may have happened.

....

....

....

....

[3]

2.2 Analyse the likely effect of the expansion on VDP's profits in its first two years.

....

....

....

....

....

....

....

....

....

....

[6]

[Total 9 marks]

Internal Expansion

Warm-Up

Draw lines to match the following methods of internal expansion with their correct description.

Method	Description
outsourcing	When a company sells products via the internet.
e-commerce	When a company gives other firms the right to sell its products or use its name, in return for a fee or a share of the profits.
franchising	When a company pays another firm to carry out tasks that it could do itself.

1 Purrfect Catz Ltd. make cat accessories. They are planning to expand their business by setting up a website to sell their products through. Explain **one** benefit and **one** drawback of expanding in this way.

....

....

....

....

....

....

[Total 4 marks]

2 Look at **Item A** below.

Item A — Chain Reaction:
Harry owns Chain Reaction, a small chain of shops that sell bicycles. Over the last two years, Chain Reaction has seen growth in its sales of 15%, and the business has become well-known in the county. Harry is now considering expanding further, either by opening a new shop or by franchising. Harry's first choice of location for his new shop would be the town of Gordale. Gordale is known for having well-paid, sporty residents, and is close to a national cycle path. However, the rent of a shop in Gordale would be much higher than for any of his current shops. Harry has recently been approached by Cathy, a woman from Gordale who is interested in starting a franchise of Chain Reaction in the town.

Recommend whether Harry should expand his business by opening a new shop, or by allowing Cathy to start a franchise. Give reasons for your advice.
Write your answer on a separate piece of paper.

[Total 9 marks]

External Expansion

1 Which of the following is the correct description of a merger?
Shade **one** oval only.

A When one firm expands by buying more than half the shares in another firm. ⬭

B When a firm expands by opening a new outlet. ⬭

C When a firm grows by expanding its own activities. ⬭

D When two firms join together to form a new firm. ⬭

[Total 1 mark]

2 Look at **Item A** below.

> **Item A — Relish the Day:**
> Relish the Day are a company that make jams and chutneys. They have recently taken over Bailes Farming Ltd., a company that had been supplying them with fruit and vegetables. Before the takeover, Bailes Farming Ltd. was struggling financially and was on the brink of closing. Relish the Day restructured the hierarchy of Bailes Farming Ltd. This involved making some staff redundant and also moving some employees from Relish the Day into management positions at Bailes Farming Ltd. Since the takeover, the newly expanded Relish the Day has seen growth in its profits of 15%.

2.1 Explain **one** reason why Relish the Day may have chosen to take over Bailes Farming Ltd.

....

....

[2]

2.2 Analyse the likely impact of the takeover on the morale of staff from Bailes Farming Ltd.

....

....

....

....

....

....

....

....

....

[6]

[Total 8 marks]

Employment and the Law

1 Which of the following statements is covered by the Equality Act 2010?
Shade **one** oval only.

A The job that a person has shouldn't affect how much they earn. ⬭

B Recruitment should not discriminate against people based on their ability. ⬭

C All employees should earn at least the national living wage. ⬭

D A person's disability should not affect their likelihood of getting a job. ⬭

[Total 1 mark]

2 In 1974, the UK government introduced the Health and Safety at Work Act. Under this act, businesses have to take responsibility for the health and safety of their employees while they are at work.

2.1 Identify **three** things that employers must do to comply with this health and safety law.

1. ....

2. ....

3. ....

[3]

2.2 Explain **one** disadvantage to businesses of following this law.

....

....

[2]

2.3 Identify **two** possible consequences for a business that doesn't follow this law.

1. ....

2. ....

[2]

[Total 7 marks]

3 By law, all employers must pay their staff at least the national minimum wage.
Explain **one** advantage and **one** disadvantage that minimum wage law has for businesses.

Advantage: ....

....

Disadvantage: ....

....

[Total 4 marks]

Consumer Law

1 There are legal requirements for the products that a business sells. Under the Consumer Rights Act 2015, consumers have legal rights if products do not meet these requirements.

1.1 Identify **three** things that customers are legally entitled to if a product does not meet legal requirements.

....

[3]

1.2 Explain **two** ways in which a business might be damaged if its products don't meet legal requirements.

1. ....

....

2. ....

....

[4]

[Total 7 marks]

2 Look at **Item A** below.

Item A — Bill's Films:
Bill has started up a business selling used DVDs, called Bill's Films. He buys 50 used DVDs and checks each one for faults. He goes through the following checklist for each DVD:

1	Does the DVD play from beginning to end without stopping?	pass/fail
2	Does the DVD case match the DVD inside?	pass/fail

If a DVD fails either of the tests above then he still sells it as it is, without labelling any defects, but at a discount price. He sells the remaining DVDs at a higher price.

2.1 Identify **two** reasons why Bill's Films is breaking consumer law.

1. ....

2. ....

[2]

2.2 Identify **two** changes that Bill can make to his business in order to keep to the requirements of consumer law.

1. ....

2. ....

[2]

[Total 4 marks]

Technology and Business

1 Identify **three** examples of different forms of digital communication.

....

[Total 3 marks]

2 Explain why it may be advantageous for a business to use digital forms of communication to contact stakeholders rather than more traditional forms of communication.

....

....

[Total 2 marks]

3 Look at **Item A** below.

Item A — Amazon®:
In 2012, the online retailer Amazon® bought a robotics company called Kiva Systems® for $775 million. *Kiva Systems* specialised in making robots for use in locating and delivering products in warehouses.

The robots receive orders from the computer database system. They are then programmed to locate the shelf with the correct products and to lift the shelf and bring it to the worker who can locate the products. *Amazon* employs members of staff to manage the robotics system.

In addition to the use of robots, *Amazon* also has an advanced computer system which tracks each product as it is packaged and labelled with an address for each customer.

3.1 Explain **one** advantage to *Amazon* of selling products online.

....

....

[2]

3.2 Identify **two** disadvantages to *Amazon* of introducing this robotics system in their warehouses.

1. ....

2. ....

[2]

3.3 Identify **two** advantages for *Amazon* in having this advanced computer system and robotics.

1. ....

2. ....

[2]

[Total 6 marks]

Ethical Considerations

1 Pharmacuticles is a firm which specialises in hair and nail beauty products. Like many companies, Pharmacuticles has its own ethical policies.

1.1 Explain **one** possible reason why Pharmacuticles has ethical policies.

....

....

[2]

1.2 Identify **two** ethical considerations that Pharmacuticles may have for its employees.

1. ....

2. ....

[2]

1.3 Identify **two** ethical considerations that Pharmacuticles may have in product development.

1. ....

2. ....

[2]

[Total 6 marks]

2 Look at **Item A** below.

Item A — Beancraft Ltd.:
Beancraft Ltd. is a UK company that makes coffee. It buys coffee beans from plantations in less economically developed countries. Unlike most of its competitors in the UK, Beancraft Ltd. only uses plantations that have been certified by a Fair Trade organisation. There are more plantations worldwide that are not fair trade certified than those that are.

Analyse the effects of using a source of coffee beans that is Fair Trade certified on the financial success of Beancraft Ltd.

....

....

....

....

....

....

....

....

....

....

[Total 6 marks]

Environmental Influences

Warm-Up

Fill in the gaps in the following passage, using the words on the right.

A company can improve its .... by ensuring that it doesn't use too many scarce resources to make products, and also by using fuels that are .... Using fuels that emit less carbon dioxide will mean that a business is contributing less to global ....

renewable
non-renewable
sustainability
warming
cooling
pollution

1 Look at **Item A** below.

Item A — ForKids:
ForKids, a company which makes plastic children's toys, has just opened a new factory near a residential area. The factory has several pieces of machinery for making toys. Recently ForKids has received a complaint from a nearby resident about the noise from the factory.

Once the toys have been made, they are packaged individually in large cardboard boxes and transported in vans to distribution centres throughout the country.

1.1 Explain **two** ways in which the managers of ForKids could minimise the impact of the new factory on the surrounding environment.

1. ....

....

2. ....

....

[4]

1.2 Explain **one** advantage to ForKids of making the new factory more environmentally friendly.

....

....

[2]

1.3 Explain **one** disadvantage to ForKids of making the new factory more environmentally friendly.

....

....

[2]

[Total 8 marks]

Exam Practice Tip

Whenever you get a context like the one in question 1 here, make sure you use as much of the information you're given as possible. The context will probably have lots of little hints for you to pick up on. Then it's your job to interpret the information and apply it to the question you're given. It's not always easy, but at least you have plenty of practice here.

Unemployment and Consumer Spending

1 Explain **one** way in which high unemployment may cause problems for a business.

[Total 2 marks]

2 Explain why businesses may **not** want to employ a person who hasn't worked for a long time.

[Total 2 marks]

3 The consumer price index represents the price of goods in a country. **Figure 1** shows the percentage change in the consumer price index and the average weekly wage in **country A** every year between 2006 and 2017.

Figure 1

Percentage change in consumer price index and average weekly wages in country A between 2006 and 2017

Percentage change
0
1
2
3
4
5
6
7
8
2006
2007
2008
2009
2010
2011
2012
2013
2014
2015
2016
2017
Year
Consumer price index
Average weekly wages

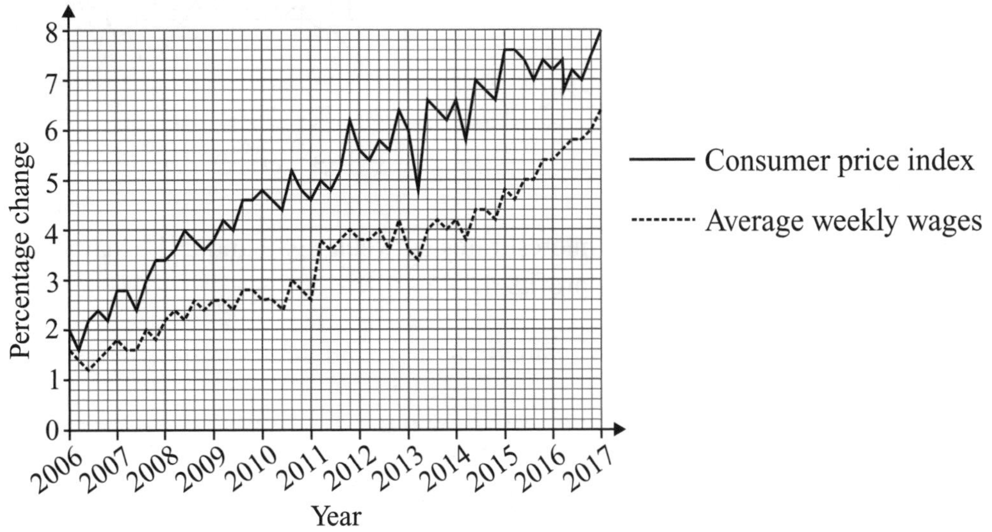

Explain how the trend shown in **Figure 1** may have affected businesses which sell luxury items in **country A** between 2006 and 2017.

MATHS SKILLS

[Total 4 marks]

Interest Rates

1 Which of the following groups will benefit most from high interest rates? Shade **one** oval only.

A People with mortgages on their houses. ⬭

B Banks that lend money to businesses. ⬭

C Small businesses that have borrowed money. ⬭

D Consumers who want to buy products. ⬭

[Total 1 mark]

2 **Figure 1** shows how yearly interest rates changed in a country between 1900 and 2010.

MATHS SKILLS

Figure 1

Yearly interest rates in country A from 1900 to 2010

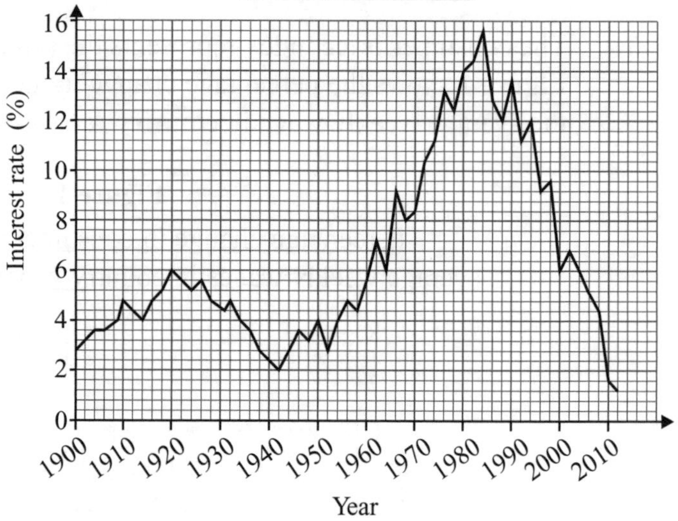

Interest rate (%): 0, 2, 4, 6, 8, 10, 12, 14, 16

Year: 1900, 1910, 1920, 1930, 1940, 1950, 1960, 1970, 1980, 1990, 2000, 2010

2.1 Explain which year was the most expensive for borrowing money.

....

....

....

....

....

[2]

2.2 Explain how the overall trend in interest rates between 1980 and 2010 may have affected consumer spending and business profits.

....

....

....

....

....

[4]

[Total 6 marks]

Exam Practice Tip

This isn't the easiest topic to get your head around, so take your time when answering these questions. For questions about the impact of changing interest rates on spending, think about what kind of effect a high or low interest rate would have on the cost of borrowing. How much people can borrow will affect what they spend.

Competition

Warm-Up

Circle true or false for each of the following statements.

All the potential customers for a product can be considered a type of market. true/false

A competitive market is one in which businesses sell very specialised products. true/false

Increased competition will mean that prices are likely to get lower. true/false

Markets which have a very high start-up cost will usually have low competition. true/false

1 Look at **Item A** below.

Item A — Bluebell Babies:
Bluebell Babies, a company specialising in child care products, spots a gap in the market for a new portable baby bath. They spend £15 000 designing and developing the new product and then sell each unit for £40 under the brand name Travel Bath.

12 months after launching their bath, they notice that three other companies have launched similar products. They also notice that the overall size of the market has grown since more parents are choosing to buy a travel bath for their baby. The prices of the different portable baby baths available in the market are shown in the bar chart on the right.

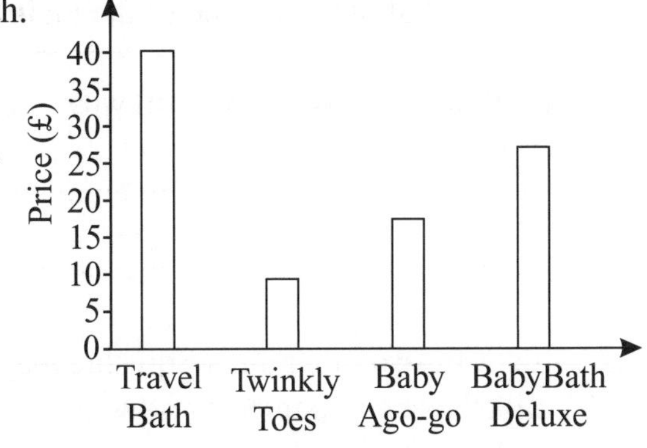

Bluebell Babies carries out market research to see how its customers view Travel Bath and its competitors' products. They find that customers consider BabyBath Deluxe to be the highest quality product and Travel Bath the second highest. They also find that only 10% of people they surveyed on the street had heard of Travel Bath, compared to 12% for Twinkly Toes, 30% for Baby Ago-go and 32% for BabyBath Deluxe.

1.1 Explain how competition within the portable baby bath market in **Item A** changed over time.

....

....

....

....

[4]

1.2 Bluebell Babies want to increase the sales and market share of Travel Bath.
Recommend which of the following actions they should take:
- Reduce the price of Travel Bath to £30.
- Invest in additional marketing material for Travel Bath.

Give reasons for your answer.
Write your answer on a separate sheet of paper.

[9]

[Total 13 marks]

Globalisation

1 Which of the following statements is true?
Shade **one** oval only.

- **A** Globalisation means that businesses can buy from and sell to many countries. ⬭
- **B** Globalisation decreases the size of the market for businesses. ⬭
- **C** Globalisation is when consumers have to travel more to buy certain products. ⬭
- **D** Globalisation means that businesses face less competition. ⬭

[Total 1 mark]

2 Look at **Item A** and **Item B** below.

> **Item A — Squishie:**
> Squishie is a UK company which makes smoothies and milkshakes. They sell their products to a global market. One of the main aims of the company is to have a great product design.

2.1 Explain **one** possible reason why one of Squishie's aims is to have great product design.

....

....

[2]

2.2 Identify **two** other aims Squishie may have in order to compete with other smoothie and milkshake companies worldwide.

1. ....

2. ....

[2]

> **Item B — Squishie:**
> Squishie has factories for making and packaging its products in Spain, and it also sources many of its ingredients from Spanish farms. The company employs workers on the minimum wage in both Spain and the UK. When it opened its factories, its workers on the minimum wage were paid €756.7 per month in Spain, and €1378.9 per month in the UK.

2.3 Explain **two** reasons why globalisation is beneficial for Squishie.

1. ....

....

2. ....

....

[4]

[Total 8 marks]

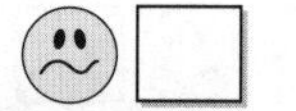

Exchange Rates

Warm-Up

Fill in the gaps in the following passage, using the words on the right.

.... are goods that are bought from a different country.

.... are goods that are sold to a different country.

If the value of the British pound decreases, British exports will be .... abroad.

more expensive
imports
exports
cheaper

1 Which of the following statements best describes what is meant by an 'exchange rate'? Shade **one** oval only.

A The price at which products are sold. ⬭

B The rate at which goods are exchanged between countries. ⬭

C The rate at which one country imports products from another. ⬭

D The price at which one currency can be traded for another. ⬭

[Total 1 mark]

2 A Chinese phone manufacturing company buys some of its raw materials from India. The company sells its products worldwide. Most of its income comes from the USA.

2.1 The value of India's currency (INR) falls against China's currency (CNY). Explain how this change in exchange rate may affect the Chinese phone manufacturing company.

....

....

....

....

[4]

2.2 The value of the USA's currency (USD) rises against China's currency (CNY). Explain how this is advantageous to the Chinese phone manufacturing company.

....

....

....

....

[4]

[Total 8 marks]

Risks in Business

1 Look at **Item A** below.

> **Item A — Tasty Teas**
> Louise is starting a new company, Tasty Teas, which sells ready cooked meals.
> In order to start up Tasty Teas, Louise has taken out a loan from her bank.
> She has decided to carry out research into what type of ready cooked meals customers would be willing to buy, and the products and prices of competitor brands.

1.1 Identify **three** reasons why Louise may have wanted to start up her own business.

1. ....

2. ....

3. ....

[3]

1.2 Explain **one** reason why borrowing money in order to start up Tasty Teas may be risky for Louise.

....

....

....

[2]

1.3 Explain **one** risk that Tasty Teas may face after it has become established.

....

....

[2]

1.4 Explain why Louise's research may reduce any risk to her business in the future.

....

....

....

[2]

1.5 Identify **two** other actions that Louise could take in order to reduce the risk to her business in the future.

1. ....

2. ....

[2]

[Total 11 marks]

> ***Exam Practice Tip***
> It can take a long time for a company to become successful, so it's really important that businesses reduce their risk as much as possible when they are just starting out. Make sure you can think of a few methods of reducing risk and that you can explain how these different methods work. And don't forget that even established businesses need to be careful.

Supply Chains

Warm-Up

Fill in the gaps in the following passage, using the words below.

customers needs manufacturers

retailers raw materials finished product

A supply chain consists of a group of firms that are involved in all the various processes required to make a finished product or service available to the .... The supply chain begins with the provider of the .... and ends with the firms that sell the .... A supply chain will typically contain suppliers, ..., distributors and retailers.

1 Which of the following defines 'logistics'?
Shade **one** oval only.

A Finding and buying things that a firm needs from suppliers outside the firm. ⬭

B Getting goods and services from one part of the supply chain to another. ⬭

C Making sure a business uses as few resources as possible and creates as little waste as possible. ⬭

D Making sure everyone in a firm takes responsibility for the quality of their work. ⬭

[Total 1 mark]

2 Identify **two** benefits to a business of managing its supply chain effectively.

1. ....

....

2. ....

....

[Total 2 marks]

3 Jemma works in procurement for a company that makes windows.
Explain, using **one** example, what her job will involve.

....

....

....

....

[Total 2 marks]

4 Identify **three** factors that could affect a business's choice of suppliers.

1. ....

2. ....

3. ....

[Total 3 marks]

5 Look at **Item A** below.

> **Item A — Shake it Up**
> Shake it Up is a company that makes milkshakes and delivers them to cafés across the UK. Shake it Up buys the milk for its milkshakes from a local farm. The factory manager can confirm how much milk he would like for the following day up to 6pm the day before. The farm always ensures that the order is ready for collection by Shake it Up's van driver the next morning. The produce from the farm is of a high standard, so Shake it Up has been buying from the farm for many years. Recently, the farm has started to offer Shake it Up a discount on orders over £500. Shake it Up buys enough to use this discount approximately once a week.

5.1 Identify **two** ways that Shake it Up would need to organise logistics in the supply chain for their milkshakes.

1. ....

....

2. ....

....

[2]

> **Item B — Shake it Up**
> The directors of Shake it Up have decided to expand the business by making ice-cream as well as milkshakes. As the product is new, they aren't sure what the demand will be. They are considering whether to use the same arrangement for buying and collecting cream from the farm as for milk, or whether to use Ribblethwaites, a larger farming corporation that they have not used before. Buying cream from Ribblethwaites would be cheaper than the local farm, but would mean Shake it Up had to order cream a week in advance. The cream would then be delivered to Shake it Up's factory.

5.2 Recommend whether Shake it Up should buy cream from the local farm or from Ribblethwaites. Give reasons for your advice.
Write your answer on a separate piece of paper.

[9]

[Total 11 marks]

> ***Exam Practice Tip***
> Choosing the right supplier, working well with suppliers and then managing the rest of the supply chain effectively will all affect the costs and efficiency of a business. And don't forget that sometimes businesses may have to make a compromise in one part of the supply chain, e.g. in the costs of raw materials, to make sure the rest of the process runs smoothly.

Methods of Production

1 Which of the following describes the term 'job production'?
Shade **one** oval only.

A When a firm manufactures unique products one at a time. ⬭

B When a firm produces items in a way that stock levels are kept to a minimum. ⬭

C When a firm produces items in a way that they have buffer stocks of items at every stage in the process. ⬭

D When a firm manufactures identical products on an assembly line. ⬭

[Total 1 mark]

2 Identify **two** disadvantages of using flow production, rather than job production, to produce goods.

1. ....

2. ....

[Total 2 marks]

3 Look at **Item A** below.

> **Item A — Sofa-So-Good Ltd.**
> Sofa-So-Good Ltd. is a sofa manufacturer that sells to furniture stores and directly to the public. One service Sofa-So-Good offers is to design and make sofas according to a customer's individual needs. They use the job production method to manufacture these sofas.

3.1 Explain **one** advantage and **one** disadvantage to Sofa-So-Good Ltd. of using job production for this service.

Advantage: ....

....

Disadvantage: ....

....

[4]

3.2 A furniture store has asked Sofa-So-Good Ltd. to produce a range of identical sofas. Explain why flow production might be a more suitable manufacturing method for these sofas.

....

....

....

[3]

[Total 7 marks]

Exam Practice Tip

The way a product is made depends on what it is and how many of the same product a company is making. Make sure you can explain the best way to produce a given product and the benefits and drawbacks of job and flow production.

Production Efficiency

Warm-Up

Draw lines to match up each of the production methods below with the correct description.

Method	Description
just-in-time	When a business aims to use as few resources as possible and have as little waste as possible.
lean production	When a company aims to keep stock levels to a bare minimum.
just-in-case	When a company makes sure it has buffer stocks of items at every stage in the process.

1 Look at **Item A** below.

> **Item A — The Reading Shelf**
> The Reading Shelf is a firm that supplies books to bookshops around the UK. Orders from bookshops can vary a lot. It manages stock using the 'just-in-case' method, and orders books in bulk from a supplier once a week. Occasionally, deliveries can be delayed. The supplier offers discounts on orders over 2000 units. The supplier has a fixed delivery charge, no matter how large the order is. The Reading Shelf stores books in a large warehouse which costs £1,500 per month to rent. So that there is space in the warehouse to store new titles of books, any copies of titles that are no longer selling are discarded at the end of each month.

1.1 Identify **two** advantages to The Reading Shelf of using the 'just-in-case' method of stock control.

1. ....

....

2. ....

....

[2]

1.2 The Reading Shelf is considering changing its method of stock control to just-in-time (JIT). Analyse how changing to just-in-time may affect the costs of The Reading Shelf.

....

....

....

....

....

....

....

....

[6]

[Total 8 marks]

Quality

1 Look at **Item A** below.

> **Item A — SB Vans**
> Saif runs SB Vans, a courier company that delivers furniture from factories to customers' homes. Saif guarantees delivery within 48 hours of the customer ordering their furniture.
> He will also set up the furniture for no extra cost. Recently, Saif employed another driver, Alec.

1.1 Identify **two** ways that Saif tries to provide a high quality service.

1. ....

2. ....

[2]

1.2 Explain **one** action Saif should have taken in order to make sure his standards of quality were maintained when Alec joined the company.

....

....

[2]

> **Item B — SB Vans**
> **Figure 1** shows how long it took for furniture to be delivered to customers in the month before and the month after Alec joined.

Figure 1

1.3 Analyse how the impact Alec has had on quality may affect SB Vans. MATHS SKILLS

....

....

....

....

....

....

....

....

[6]

[Total 10 marks]

Quality Management

1 Identify **one** problem with maintaining quality for each of the following methods of expansion:

Outsourcing: ....

....

Franchising: ....

....

[Total 2 marks]

2 Look at **Item A** below.

> **Item A — Toyota**
> Toyota manufactures cars. One of Toyota's aims is to have high levels of customer satisfaction. They do this using a system of Total Quality Management.
> Two of their methods for maintaining quality are shown below:
> - Each person on the production line aims to ensure that the work they are passing on doesn't have any problems. If it does, they can stop the production line in order to fix the problem.
> - Each day, a number of the cars produced are tested further on a test track.
>
> Toyota have won a number of awards for quality since using Total Quality Management.

2.1 Explain how the methods described in **Item A** help Toyota to maintain the quality of their cars.

....

....

....

....

[2]

2.2 Analyse the possible impact of using Total Quality Management (TQM) at Toyota.

....

....

....

....

....

....

....

....

....

[6]

[Total 8 marks]

Customer Service

Warm-Up

Put the following parts of the sales process in order from earliest to latest.

Approaching customers. Finding customers. Getting the customer to buy the item.

Presenting the product to a customer. Following up with the customer after the sale. Assessing customer needs.

1. .... earliest
2. ....
3. ....
4. ....
5. ....
6. .... latest

1 Which of the following is a form of post-sales service?
Shade **one** oval only.

A Training customers in how to use the product. ⬭

B Getting the contact details of potential customers. ⬭

C Providing customers with information about the product they're interested in. ⬭

D Calling customers to find out if they're interested in a product. ⬭

[Total 1 mark]

2 Customer service has benefits for businesses and their customers.

2.1 Explain how good customer service can affect how a business prices its products.

....

....

....

[2]

2.2 Explain how an increase in a firm's spending on customer service can lead to an increase in profits.

....

....

....

....

[3]

[Total 5 marks]

3 Look at **Item A** below.

> **Item A — Durrell's**
> Durrell's is a firm that sells electrical kitchen appliances over the phone.
> 75% of the firm's products are dispatched within four days of the given dispatch date.
> The firm offers free returns for any items that its customers wish to send back.
> The firm's customer support helpline currently answers 70% of customer calls that are made.

3.1 Explain **one** way in which Durrell's provides good customer service.

....

....

....

[2]

3.2 Explain **one** way in which Durrell's could improve its customer service.

....

....

....

....

[3]

> **Item B — Durrell's**
> Durrell's are considering setting up a website. The website would have an online shop. At the same time as launching the website, Durrell's would launch accounts on social media. Durrell's have predicted that the website could lead to a 30% increase in orders, and using social media could cause a 40% increase in customer enquiries.

3.3 Identify **two** ways in which Durrell's could use its website to provide customer service, other than using it to sell products.

1. ....

2. ....

[2]

3.4 Analyse the impact of setting up the website and social media accounts on Durrell's reputation. In your answer you should consider:

- Ways customer service will be improved
- Problems Durrell's could have with providing customer service

You must evaluate whether the overall effect on Durrell's reputation will be positive or negative. Use evidence to support your answer.
Write your answer on a separate piece of paper.

[12]

[Total 19 marks]

> ***Exam Practice Tip***
> If customers don't like a company, they won't buy their products, and they're likely to tell their friends not to as well. So knowing how to please customers with good customer service is important for companies, as well as for your exams.

Internal Organisational Structures

Warm-Up

Draw circles to show whether the statements below are **true** or **false**.

1) The number of people in each layer of a hierarchy generally decreases as you move up the hierarchy. TRUE / FALSE
2) Large firms tend to have taller organisational structures than small firms. TRUE / FALSE
3) Directors are found at the top of a firm's chain of command. TRUE / FALSE
4) As a firm's organisational structure becomes taller, it loses layers of management. TRUE / FALSE

1 Which of these statements describes a benefit of delegation? Shade **one** oval only.

A People in the top layers of a hierarchy don't have many responsibilities. ⬭

B Directors in the company have all the responsibility for tasks. ⬭

C Managers can pass tasks on to supervisors. ⬭

D Operatives are given no responsibilities. ⬭

[Total 1 mark]

2 Explain **one** disadvantage of a firm having a decentralised structure.

....

....

....

....

[Total 2 marks]

3 Explain **one** reason why it can be a problem for a business if managers have a wide span of control.

....

....

....

....

[Total 2 marks]

4 Look at **Item A** and **Figure 1** below.

Item A — Houghton & Son Ltd:
Houghton & Son Ltd. make play equipment for gardens. They have a chain of stores across the UK. Part of the firm's hierarchy is shown in **Figure 1**.
A director in Houghton & Son Ltd. feels the firm's chains of command have become too long.
He has suggested delayering the business.

Figure 1

Houghton & Son Ltd.

Claire Wilkinson
UK Sales Director
↓
Andrew Gibson
Regional Sales Manager
↓
Anjali Bhat
District Sales Manager
↓
James Lake
Branch Sales Manager
↓
Liam McNulty
Branch Sales Supervisor
↓
Omar Maarouf
Salesperson

4.1 Explain how the responsibilities of Claire Wilkinson are likely to be different from the responsibilities of Liam McNulty.

....

....

....

....

....

[2]

4.2 Explain **one** disadvantage to a firm of having long chains of command.

....

....

....

[2]

4.3 Explain why Houghton & Son Ltd.'s chains of command have grown longer as the business has grown.

....

....

....

[2]

4.4 Explain which employees of Houghton & Son would be most affected if the firm decides to delayer its hierarchy.

....

....

....

....

[3]

[Total 9 marks]

5 Look at **Item B, Figure 2** and **Figure 3** below.

Item B — CraftyCakes:
CraftyCakes is a firm that sells baked goods, such as cakes and pastries. It is a large business and many large retailers stock its products. It also owns several coffee shops. CraftyCakes are considering changing their organisational structure. Part of their current structure is shown in **Figure 2** and part of the organisational structure they are considering changing to is shown in **Figure 3**. Dotted lines show where each figure is incomplete.

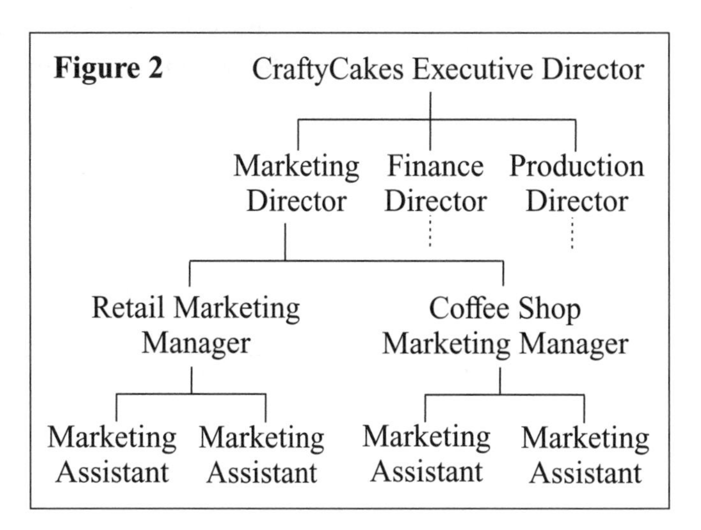

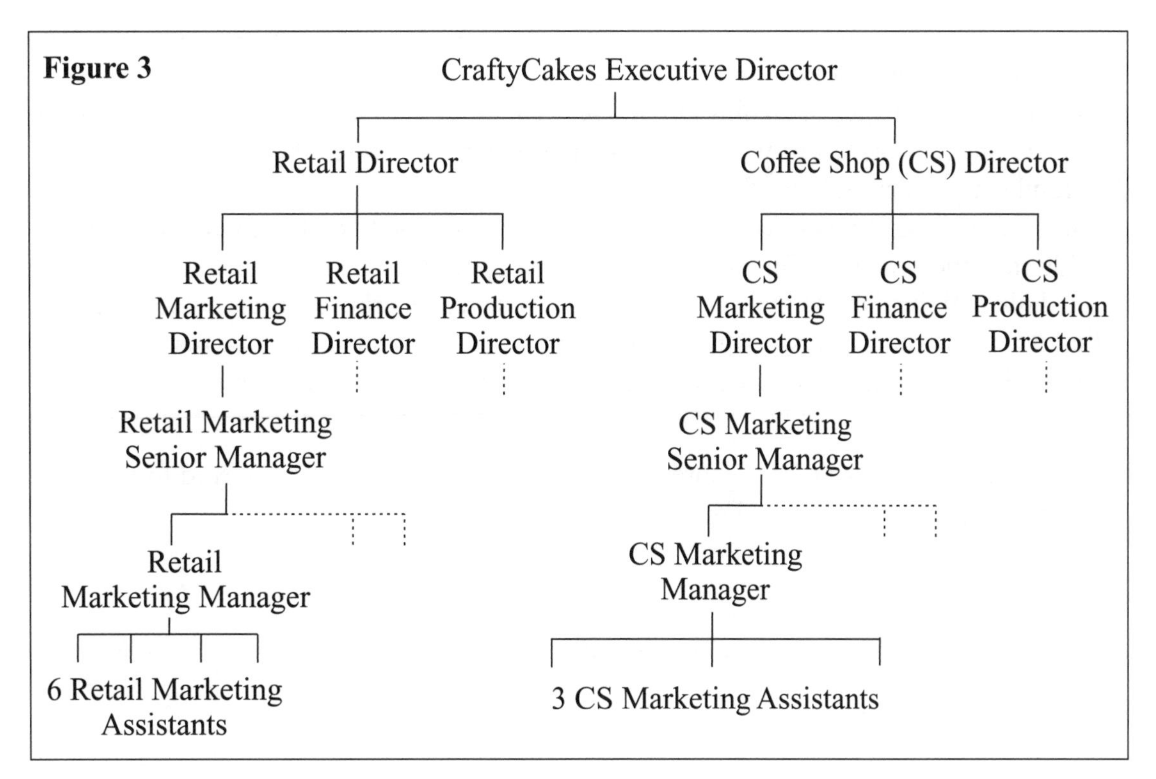

Analyse the impact of changing to the organisational structure shown in **Figure 3**.
In your answer you should consider:

- The appropriateness of each structure.
- Communication within the business.

You must evaluate which structure will be most beneficial to CraftyCakes.
Use evidence to support your answer.

Write your answer on a separate sheet of paper.

[Total 12 marks]

Exam Practice Tip

Organisational structures can look pretty scary — there are lines and job titles all over the place. If you get given one in an exam question take time to look at it closely and work out what it's showing you. Pay particular attention to people's job titles, how many layers the structure has and how many people are in each layer.

Contracts of Employment

1 Explain **one** difference between a part-time contract of employment and a zero hour contract of employment.

[Total 2 marks]

2 Look at **Item A** below.

> **Item A — Cheeky Bees:**
> Simon is the manager of a children's nursery called Cheeky Bees. He employs three nursery supervisors, all of whom work 40 hours per week when the nursery is open (Monday to Friday, 8:30am-5:30pm).
> One of the nursery supervisors, Carla, is currently pregnant and has to attend regular midwife appointments. On the days of Carla's appointments, Simon has to restructure the daily activities in the nursery to cover her absence. Carla has already told Simon that when she returns to work after having the baby she wants to reduce her hours. Simon is considering asking Carla whether she would like to job share on her return.

2.1 Explain why it may have been more beneficial for Simon to have employed four nursery supervisors, each working 30 hours a week.

[2]

2.2 Identify **one** advantage to both Simon and Carla of Carla being in a job share on her return to work.

Simon:

Carla:

[2]

[Total 4 marks]

Exam Practice Tip

Contracts of employment aren't too tricky really — but don't let that fool you into thinking you don't need to learn the details. Make sure you're really clear on the differences between full-time, part-time, zero hour and job share contracts.

Recruitment

1 Which of these statements describes a job analysis?
Shade **one** oval only.

A A written description of the personal qualities needed to do a job. ⬭

B A process in which a firm thinks in depth about every little detail of a job. ⬭

C A form a candidate for a job has to fill in before an interview. ⬭

D A process managers go through when deciding which candidate to select for a job. ⬭

[Total 1 mark]

2 Identify **two** pieces of information that would be included in a job description.

1. ....

2. ....

[Total 2 marks]

3 Look at **Item A** below.

> **Item A — Calm Days:**
> Jasmine owns Calm Days — a chain of beauty salons. She currently has a vacancy for a nail technician in one of her salons. She is looking for someone who already has some experience in a similar role and who will fit into the chatty, informal environment of her salons. She has advertised the vacancy on an employment website and has had lots of people applying for the job. She has made a shortlist of the candidates she is going to invite for an interview and tests.

3.1 Identify **two** things Jasmine may have asked candidates to send to her in order to apply for the job.

1. ....

2. ....

[2]

3.2 Jasmine didn't include a person specification in her advert. Explain why this may have been useful.

....

....

[2]

3.3 Explain why interviews and testing will help Jasmine to find the sort of person she is looking for.

....

....

....

....

....

[4]

[Total 8 marks]

4 Look at **Item B** below.

Item B — Chem and Co:
Chem and Co are a pharmaceutical company. They need to recruit a team of senior chemists to help them develop a new drug. They are planning to advertise the roles on a specialist science recruitment website.

4.1 Identify **two** qualities Chem and Co may look for when selecting candidates for the new roles.

1. ....

2. ....

[2]

4.2 Explain **two** advantages to Chem and Co of advertising the roles externally rather than internally.

1. ....

....

2. ....

....

[4]

[Total 6 marks]

5 Look at **Item C** below.

Item C — The Horse and Foal:
The Horse and Foal is a village pub. In recent years the pub has been losing customers as people are preferring to spend more time in other nearby pubs. The owners of the Horse and Foal regularly need to recruit new bar and kitchen staff to replace workers that have chosen to leave. The owners rarely advertise the jobs — instead they are usually filled by family and friends of existing staff members. This allows the roles to be filled quickly and means the owners don't have to spend time and money producing job adverts. However, the owners have been advised that this method of recruitment may be damaging the business in the long run.

Analyse the benefit to the business of spending more time and money on recruitment.

....

....

....

....

....

....

....

....

....

[Total 6 marks]

Staff Training

Warm-Up

Draw lines to connect each type of training on the left to its description on the right.

on-the-job training	This training introduces new workers to the company before they start the job.
off-the-job training	This training is done in the workplace once the person has started the job.
induction training	This training often happens away from a person's workplace.

1 Explain **two** benefits of training employees for a business.

1. ....

....

....

2. ....

....

....

[Total 4 marks]

2 SilkiSoft is a company that produces video games. It sometimes sends its programming staff to courses at a local university to learn new skills, such as new programming techniques.

2.1 Explain why courses at the university are a more appropriate form of training for SilkiSoft's programming staff than on-the-job training.

....

....

....

[2]

2.2 Explain **one** disadvantage to SilkiSoft of training its staff at the university rather than using on-the-job training.

....

....

....

[2]

[Total 4 marks]

Financial Motivation

1 Explain the difference between a salary and a wage.

....

....

....

[Total 2 marks]

2 Explain the benefit to a firm of enrolling their staff in a profit sharing scheme.

....

....

....

[Total 2 marks]

3 Look at **Item A** below.

Item A — Packman's Glazing:
Packman's Glazing is a business that sells doors and windows. They pay their junior sales staff an annual salary of £15 000. On top of their salary, sales staff also get 5% commission on each sale they make.
In recent months, Packman's Glazing have lost two of their junior sales staff to a new, rival firm. One of the factors that persuaded the staff to move was the rival firm's pay scheme. They don't pay sales commission, but they pay junior sales staff an annual salary of £24 000. The owners of Packman's Glazing are considering whether to move to a similar pay scheme to avoid losing any more staff.

3.1 Drew is a junior salesman at Packman's Glazing. In March his sales totalled £19 000. Calculate the total amount that Drew would have been paid in March before tax.

MATHS SKILLS

£ ....

[3]

3.2 Recommend whether Packman's Glazing should stay with their salary and commission pay scheme or move to a pay scheme similar to that of the new, rival firm.
Give reasons for your answer.

Write your answer on a separate sheet of paper.

[9]

[Total 12 marks]

Non-Financial Motivation

1 Explain how staff can be motivated by being given the opportunity to learn new skills.

....

....

[Total 2 marks]

2 Look at **Item A** below.

Item A — Meera's Shoes:
Meera is the manager of a shoe shop called Meera's Shoes. She employs twelve members of staff, but does not consult them about the decisions she makes as a manager. Meera has a very strict training programme, in which she monitors new staff members closely until she is confident they understand everything they need to do in their role. Every month Meera holds a staff meeting with her employees. The meeting gives employees a chance to voice their opinions and ask Meera questions. The meeting always ends with Meera awarding one staff member an employee of the month badge based on who she thinks has made the most positive contribution to the business within the last month.

2.1 Explain, using an example, how Meera could use fringe benefits to motivate her employees.

....

....

[2]

2.2 Analyse how Meera's management style and actions are likely to affect her staff's motivation.

....

....

....

....

....

....

....

....

....

[6]

[Total 8 marks]

Exam Practice Tip
Don't worry if you get given information in the exam about a method of motivation that you haven't heard of before. Just remember, motivational methods all have the same, basic outcome — they make workers feel more valued, better rewarded and generally happier to go to work each day. This can make workers more productive and less likely to leave.

The Marketing Mix

1 Look at **Item A** below.

> **Item A — WorkOut Ltd.:**
> Ananda owns a sportswear company, WorkOut Ltd. He spends a large amount of money researching customer preferences in sportswear and ensuring that customers who own his products enjoy them and find them attractive. His products are relatively expensive. His brand is not very well known except amongst fitness experts. He sells his products directly to the owners of gyms, who are then responsible for selling the products to the customers in their gyms.

Identify which **two** aspects of the marketing mix have been prioritised by Ananda.

1. ....

2. ....

[Total 2 marks]

2 Look at **Item B** below.

> **Item B — Williamson's:**
> Williamson's is an established kitchenware store in a shopping centre. It sells high quality kitchen goods, including pots, pans, cutlery, crockery and items used for baking. Each product is sold with a 15% profit margin. Most of the customers who visit the store come because they have heard about it from friends.
>
> Recently, a competitor kitchenware store, DiscountDishes, opened in the same shopping centre as Williamson's. DiscountDishes sells similar items to Williamson's but at a lower price, and slightly lower quality. It doesn't sell certain specialty items that Williamson's sells.
>
> DiscountDishes has posters up at the entrance to the shopping centre and is offering a free spatula to any customer who spends over £15 in store.

2.1 Explain how Williamson's products contribute to it having a successful marketing mix.

....

....

[2]

2.2 Analyse the impact the opening of DiscountDishes may have on the following aspects of Williamson's marketing mix:

- Price
- Promotion

You must evaluate which aspect will be affected most. Use evidence to support your answer.
Write your answer on a separate sheet of paper.

[12]

[Total 14 marks]

Market Research

1 Which of the following explains what is meant by the market share of a business? Shade **one** oval only.

A The proportion of total sales within a market that is controlled by the business. ⬭

B The number of potential customers for the business. ⬭

C The number of segments of the market that the business controls. ⬭

D The number of individuals in the business. ⬭

[Total 1 mark]

2 Businesses use segmentation to identify their target market.

2.1 Explain, using an example, what is meant by 'segmentation'.

....

....

....

[2]

2.2 Explain why it's important for a business to correctly identify their target market.

....

....

....

[2]

[Total 4 marks]

3 Davis and Sons is a business that sells suits. Davis and Sons decide to carry out market research on their competitors. They also study the demand for different suit colours in the market, in order to understand their customers' needs.

3.1 Identify **two** pieces of information that they could try to collect about their competitors.

....

[2]

3.2 Identify **two** reasons why understanding customer needs is important.

1. ....

....

2. ....

....

[2]

[Total 4 marks]

Types of Market Research

1 Which of the following is an example of primary market research? Shade **one** oval only.

A using an article in a magazine ⬭

B an interview ⬭

C researching the market on the internet ⬭

D using government publications ⬭

[Total 1 mark]

2 A business is creating a new magazine for people over the age of 70. It decides to carry out a number of focus groups before making the magazine.

2.1 Explain **one** factor that should be considered when carrying out the focus groups.

....

....

[2]

2.2 Identify **two** advantages of using focus groups over other forms of primary research.

1. ....

2. ....

[2]

[Total 4 marks]

3 Look at **Item A** below.

> **Item A — Jack's Snacks:**
> Jackie is starting a small business making and delivering sandwiches to cafes in her local area. She decides to carry out some secondary and primary market research into customer preferences and the sales of different types of sandwiches from the different cafes in the area.

3.1 Explain why a small business might prefer using secondary market research to primary research.

....

....

[2]

3.2 Identify **two** disadvantages of carrying out secondary research.

1. ....

2. ....

[2]

3.3 Recommend whether Jackie should carry out interviews of local business owners or use an online questionnaire on her website to add to her market research. Give reasons for your advice.
Write your answer on a separate sheet of paper.

[9]

[Total 13 marks]

Using Market Research

Warm-Up

Circle qualitative or quantitative to show what type of data each of the following is.

The percentage increase in profits for a business.	qualitative/quantitative
Customer opinions on the quality of service from a waiter.	qualitative/quantitative
Customer scores for products out of a maximum of five.	qualitative/quantitative
A graph showing the variation in sales of a product throughout a year.	qualitative/quantitative

1 Look at **Item A** below.

Item A — Tom's Teas:

Tom's Teas is a tea shop. Tom, the owner, has blended three new herbal teas to sell in his shop. He decides to carry out some market research to find out which of the teas is likely to be most successful.

Tom offers free samples of each tea in the cafe and asks customers to fill in a short questionnaire about them. The questionnaire is shown on the right.

Q1 Which of the three herbal teas did you prefer?
- Jasmine deluxe ☐
- Camomile and nettle ☐
- Liquorice and mint ☐
- Didn't like any of them ☐

Q2 Was there any tea that you really disliked? Please explain your answer.

Q3 Would you buy one of these teas instead of another drink in the shop?

78% of the people who responded to the questionnaire preferred the Jasmine deluxe tea, 10% preferred the camomile and nettle tea, 4% preferred the liquorice and mint tea and 8% didn't like any of them. A common answer to question 2 was that the liquorice and mint tea tasted bitter; however, there were few complaints about the other two teas. 52% of the people who responded to the questionnaire stated "No" for question 3.

Analyse how this market research is likely to affect the products that Tom's Teas offers.

....

....

....

....

....

....

....

....

....

....

[Total 6 marks]

2 Look at **Item B** below.

Item B — The RiverHouse Restaurant:

Georgina owns a restaurant called The RiverHouse Restaurant. The restaurant is in an old building, with oak beams and a large log fire. It is based on a country lane next to a river. She recently carried out a survey of some of her customers. She carried out the same survey five years previously. The results for one of the questions on her survey are shown below.

Q1 What is the most important aspect of a restaurant for you?

- the choice of food
- the atmosphere
- the location
- the price

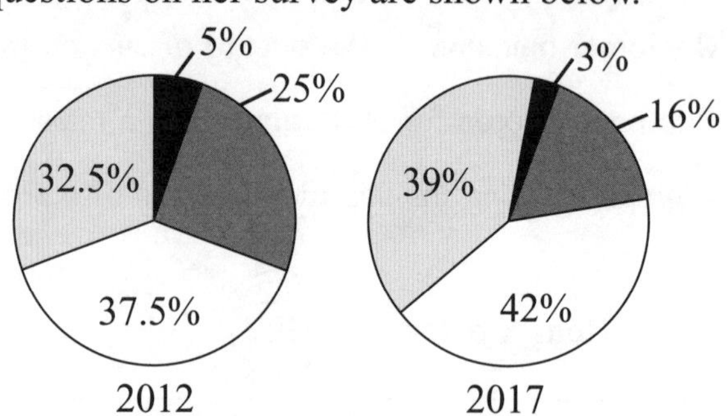

Before the survey, Georgina had flyers for her restaurant that showed a picture of the outside of the restaurant and displayed the price of her set menu. Afterwards, she changed her flyers to show an image of the inside, and a list of live music events that she is hosting.

2.1 Analyse the effect changing her flyers is likely to have on Georgina's sales.

....

....

....

....

....

....

....

....

....

[6]

2.2 Georgina is considering two options for improving her business:

- Improving the decorations and furniture inside the restaurant.
- Increasing the number of choices on the menu.

Recommend which is the better option for Georgina. Give reasons for your advice.
Write your answer on a separate sheet of paper.

[9]

[Total 15 marks]

Exam Practice Tip

There's no easy way around these longer questions, you've just got to pay attention to all of the information you've been given. Then you can use it, as well as a bit of business knowledge, to recommend the most sensible option for a business.

Product Life Cycles

1 Which of the following is **not** a phase during the product life cycle?
Shade **one** oval only.

A adolescence ⬭

B introduction ⬭

C decline ⬭

D maturity ⬭

[Total 1 mark]

2 Look at **Item A** below.

> **Item A — Leafery Ltd.:**
> A company which specialises in garden equipment, Leafery Ltd., developed a brand new weedkiller designed to selectively kill only certain types of plants. The company spent a significant amount of time and money in developing the new weedkiller and also in designing and producing a marketing campaign for it.
>
> As soon as the product was released, TV advertisements for the product were broadcast to four different regions in the UK, at 10 am every day, for two weeks. The company also purchased advertising space in two of the major gardening magazines published throughout the UK, for 4 months starting 6 months after the product was introduced. They placed coupons for a free bottle of the weedkiller in the gardening magazines. They also started by charging a low price for the weedkiller with only a small profit per item sold.

2.1 Explain what happens during the development stage of a product's life cycle.

....

....

[2]

2.2 Analyse how you would expect the marketing mix of the weedkiller shown in **Item A** to change as the product entered the maturity phase of its life cycle.

....

....

....

....

....

....

....

....

[6]

[Total 8 marks]

Extension Strategies

1 RSI Gaming Ltd. make games consoles. One of their products, the AddictaBox, is in the decline phase of its lifecycle. The AddictaBox is quite old and doesn't work with some of the new games in the market.

Explain why RSI Gaming Ltd. may decide to lower the price of the AddictaBox.

[Total 4 marks]

2 Look at **Item A** below.

> **Item A — Nestlé®:**
> Nestlé® KitKat® chocolate bars were among the most popular chocolate bars in the UK for many years. However, since the late 1990s their popularity has fallen due to other competitor brands taking over the market.
> To extend the life of the *KitKat* brand, *Nestlé* launched a new variation on the product called a *KitKat* Chunky. They also made the chocolate bars available in different flavours, including orange and mint. This allowed *KitKat* to remain among the five most popular chocolate bars in the market.
> However, in 2014 sales of *KitKat* decreased compared to the previous year, and other biscuit brands increased their market share. *Nestlé* spent £10m on marketing *KitKat* in 2015, including launching a partnership with the online video channel YouTube. It created new packaging with a link to online videos that the consumer could watch while enjoying their *KitKat*. After the campaign was launched, market research firm YouGov found via its daily BrandIndex service that the proportion of UK consumers 18+ who had bought a *KitKat* in the last 30 days had increased from 11% to 17%.

Analyse the effectiveness of the different extension strategies used by *Nestlé* in **Item A**.

[Total 6 marks]

Product Portfolios

1 Explain why a business would aim to have a balanced product portfolio.

....

....

[Total 2 marks]

2 Squeezyclean is a company which sells cleaning products.
It has three products (A, B and C) currently on sale.
Figure 1 shows where A, B and C are placed on a Boston Matrix.

Figure 1

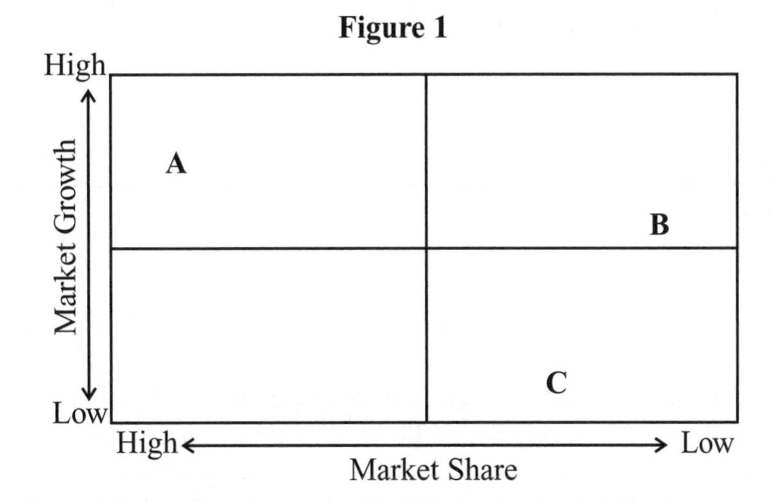

2.1 Explain which Squeezyclean product has only recently been launched.

....

....

[3]

2.2 Explain which Squeezyclean product is a "star" on the Boston Matrix.

....

....

[3]

2.3 Squeezyclean notice that one of their products is classified as a "dog" on the Boston Matrix.
Explain why this may be a problem for the company.

....

....

[3]

2.4 Explain what is meant by a "cash cow" product on a Boston Matrix.

....

....

[2]

[Total 11 marks]

Product Development

Warm-Up

Circle which of the following factors that a company should consider when designing a new product.

customer preferences

the cost of the product

competitors' designs

how effective an extension strategy is

where it is on the Boston Matrix

1 What is a USP? Shade **one** oval only.

A unique selling price ⬭

B unusually shaped product ⬭

C unique selling point ⬭

D unsuccessful product ⬭

[Total 1 mark]

2 Awoocar are a car company. They currently only make one model of car. It is a small car with a one-litre engine, and is available in four colours.

2.1 Awoocar are thinking of expanding their product portfolio. Explain why it is important for Awoocar to study the target market of their cars before creating new products.

....

....

....

[3]

2.2 One of the directors of Awoocar wants to develop a new car to compete in the luxury car market. Explain why this approach might be risky for Awoocar.

....

....

....

[3]

2.3 Explain **one** potential benefit for Awoocar of developing a luxury car model.

....

....

....

[2]

[Total 8 marks]

3 A company analyses its product portfolio and creates a Boston Matrix to show how well each of its products are performing. It finds that it has three "cash cows", two "dogs" and three "question marks".

3.1 Explain **one** reason why the company may be in a good position to create more products.

....

....

[2]

3.2 Explain **two** reasons why it may not be a good idea for the company to invest money in creating more products.

1. ....

....

2. ....

....

[4]

[Total 6 marks]

4 A popular haircare company is trying to expand its range of products. They have researched and developed a new conditioner.

4.1 Explain why it's important that the new conditioner matches the company's overall brand image.

....

....

....

[3]

4.2 Explain how giving the conditioner a scent not found in competitor conditioners may increase sales.

....

....

[2]

4.3 Explain why the haircare company performed intensive testing on the new conditioner before releasing it into the market.

....

....

....

[3]

[Total 8 marks]

Exam Practice Tip

A surprising amount of thought goes into packaging and promoting products to make sure they sell as well as possible. So make sure you remember that when you're thinking about product development — it's not just about developing the product so that it's as good as possible at a reasonable price, it's also about making it look really good.

Price

1 Which of the following is an **internal** factor which affects how a business prices its products? Shade **one** oval only.

A the cost of wages ⬭
B the type of market ⬭
C the competitiveness of the market ⬭
D the cost of raw materials ⬭

[Total 1 mark]

2 Look at **Item A** below.

Item A — Pottery Wheel:
Jerome runs Pottery Wheel, a small pottery company. He employs a small team of potters and sellers, rents a studio and a warehouse and owns several pieces of pottery-making equipment.

He regularly orders clay and glazes for his team. The prices his suppliers offer for clay orders are shown in **Figure 1**. He generally orders 100 kg of clay at a time.

Figure 1

Size of order	100 kg	250 kg	500 kg
Price (£)	50	110	200
Average price per kg (£)	0.5	0.44	0.4

Jerome's team make four different collections of products. Their first collection "Indigo Night" has been declining in popularity. Their newest collection "Crystal Gold" is of better quality than their other collections. It is being targeted at a more luxurious market than the other collections.

2.1 Explain why Jerome may be able to lower the prices of the pottery collections as the business starts producing more units.

....

....

....

....

[4]

2.2 Explain why Jerome may choose to lower the pricing of "Indigo Night" in the future.

....

....

[2]

2.3 Explain why the Crystal Gold collection may be priced differently to the other collections.

....

....

....

[2]

[Total 8 marks]

Pricing Strategies

1 What is the name of the pricing strategy in which a product is sold at a price **lower** than its cost? Shade **one** oval only.

A price skimming ⬭

B loss leader ⬭

C competitive pricing ⬭

D cost-plus pricing ⬭

[Total 1 mark]

2 Explain when a company may choose to use a competitive pricing strategy.

....

....

....

....

[Total 3 marks]

3 Look at **Item A** below.

> **Item A — Video Streaming Services**
> There are three major companies which offer film streaming services over the internet in a country: Video Box Ltd., which has a market share of 2%, WebFilms, which has a market share of 60%, and WatchIt Ltd., which has a market share of 35%. The average price for a streaming service is £8 per month. One of the companies has decided to charge subscribers £5 per month for the first 6 months that they use the service.

3.1 Explain what type of pricing strategy is being used by the company which is charging £5 per month.

....

....

[2]

3.2 Explain which of the companies is likely to have changed to charging £5 per month. MATHS SKILLS

....

....

....

....

[3]

[Total 5 marks]

4 Look at **Item B** below.

Item B — ElectricPages Ltd.:
A new company, ElectricPages Ltd. has just released “EezyReadr”, a new type of e-reading device for reading electronic books. Unlike other e-readers in the market, it uses a special type of e-paper which reflects natural light like normal paper and is in full colour.

E-readers can be used to store many different electronic books. Users purchasing an EezyReadr also create an account which allows them to purchase electronic books and magazines from ElectricPages Ltd.’s website. The e-books on the website can only be used with ElectricPages Ltd.’s devices, and the new EezyReadr is also not compatible with e-books from other companies.

It costs £55 to make one EezyReadr. The price of other e-reading devices on the market range from £60-£300. Individual e-books are cheap to produce. The company sell e-books with a 70% mark-up.

4.1 The average unit cost of producing an e-book is £4.40.
Calculate the price ElectricPages Ltd. will charge for each e-book.

Price = £ ....

[2]

4.2 Explain why a cost-plus pricing strategy is suitable for ElectricPages Ltd.’s e-books.

....

....

....

....

....

[3]

4.3 ElectricPages Ltd. is considering the following pricing strategies for its new EezyReadr:

- Loss leader
- Price skimming

Recommend which strategy ElectricPages Ltd. should use to establish EezyReadr on the market.
Give reasons for your advice.
Write your answer on a separate piece of paper.

[9]

[Total 14 marks]

Exam Practice Tip

You never know what might come up in a context, so be prepared for some unfamiliar material. Remember, you’re not being tested on, e.g. how much you know about e-readers, instead you just need to be able to use your own knowledge of pricing strategies as best you can for a given context. Make sure you’re confident on how to structure long answers too.

Methods of Promotion

Warm-Up

Match each form of advertising on the left with **one** of the advantages on the right. Each advantage can only be selected **once**.

Internet advert	It can target a specialist market.
Billboard	It can stay in place for a long time.
Magazine advert	It can include a link to a firm's website.

1 Identify **two** reasons why a firm may want to promote a product that has been on the market for a number of years.

1. ....

2. ....

[Total 2 marks]

2 Explain why a business might choose to sponsor an event.

....

....

....

[Total 2 marks]

3 Mamo Ltd. is an established company. One year it performs very well and decides that it can afford to develop and promote a new brand of baby food.

3.1 Identify **three** factors that Mamo Ltd. will have to consider when promoting its new product.

1. ....

2. ....

3. ....

[3]

3.2 One of the managers at Mamo Ltd. decides to do an interview with Little One magazine, in order to promote the new product. Explain **one** disadvantage of this type of promotion.

....

....

[2]

[Total 5 marks]

4 Look at **Item A** below.

Item A — Beth's Kitchen:
Bethany has recently opened a new luxury catering company, Beth's Kitchen. Bethany is the only member of office staff. The rest of the staff are involved in cooking and serving food. The business has very well qualified chefs and it caters for weddings and other formal events. Bethany takes bookings for her company mainly through the company's website.

She recently exhibited at a wedding show with some of the members of her team. While at the wedding show, she gave out free samples of food to customers, along with flyers that showed the different packages offered by the company. She also had a competition where customers gave their contact details in return for being entered into a prize draw to win a discount on one of the packages.

After the show, Bethany had a number of people book her company to cater at their weddings. She notices that after weddings, customers often post pictures and reviews of her catering service online.

4.1 Identify **two** ways in which Bethany and her team used sales promotion.

1. ....

2. ....

[2]

4.2 Explain **one** possible disadvantage of Bethany using sales promotion at the wedding show.

....

....

[2]

4.3 Bethany decides to set up a social media account for the company, in order to promote it further. Analyse how effective using a social media account to promote Beth's Kitchen would be.

....

....

....

....

....

....

....

....

....

[6]

[Total 10 marks]

Exam Practice Tip

There's quite a lot to remember for promotion — that's because there are so many different ways of doing it. To make things easier, just think about the types of promotion that you see around you every day — when it's used, what for, etc.

Place

1 Which of the following describes what is meant by "telesales"? Shade **one** oval only.

A Selling products over the phone. ⬭

B Selling electronic products, such as televisions. ⬭

C Discounts on electronic products. ⬭

D Selling products to retailers. ⬭

[Total 1 mark]

2 Lisa is setting up a small business selling handmade cushions and other small furniture accessories. She designs and makes each product herself — on average, she can produce three items per day.

2.1 Explain why selling to a wholesaler might not be suitable for Lisa's business.

....

....

[2]

2.2 Lisa decides to sell her products directly to her customers.
Explain **one** disadvantage for Lisa of selling products directly to her customers.

....

....

[2]

[Total 4 marks]

3 Look at **Item A** below.

Item A — E-Fixing:
Eric is the manager of a technology manufacturer, E-Fixing. His business manufactures spare parts for laptops and computers. They are based in Newcastle and sell directly to customers in the area. After an increase in sales, Eric decides to expand the business.
He rents a warehouse for excess stock. He also contacts a wholesaler that sells to retailers around the country and two local retailers to discuss selling his stock through these channels instead of directly to customers.
The companies provide him with the information shown in **Figure 1**, including how much stock they would be willing to buy each month and the average price they would offer Eric per unit.

Figure 1

	Amount of stock (units) per month	Average price per unit (£)
Wholesaler	1400	50
Retailer A	400	70
Retailer B	600	80

Recommend whether Eric should sell his products through the wholesaler or through the retailers. Give reasons for your advice.
Write your answer on a separate piece of paper.

[Total 9 marks]

E-commerce

Warm-Up

Circle the transactions below which are a type of **m-commerce**.

Paying a credit card bill using a desktop computer.

Buying an app using a smartphone.

Using a tablet to order groceries.

Using an e-reader to buy an e-book.

Paying for clothes in store using a credit card.

1 Which of the following statements about e-commerce is false?
Shade **one** oval only.

A M-commerce is a type of e-commerce. ⬭

B Selling an item using a website is a type of e-commerce. ⬭

C All transactions involving debit cards are a type of e-commerce. ⬭

D E-commerce always involves use of the internet. ⬭

[Total 1 mark]

2 Look at **Item A** below.

Item A — British Bikes Ltd.:
British Bikes Ltd. is a UK company which makes and sells bicycles and bicycle accessories. It has recently developed a new website and a mobile phone app that allows customers to buy products from the company. Its competitors also have similar apps available.

2.1 Explain how British Bikes have used m-commerce.

....

....

[2]

2.2 Explain **one** possible effect of using m-commerce on the sales of British Bikes Ltd.

....

....

[2]

2.3 Explain **one** reason why it's important that British Bikes Ltd. keeps developing its website and app.

....

....

[2]

[Total 6 marks]

3 Look at **Item B** and **Figure 1** below.

Item B — Topstitch:
Topstitch is a high street chain selling clothes and accessories in stores across the UK. In 2011, the company created a brand new, professionally designed website. The website contains the entire catalogue of products for the company as well as links to buy individual items. The company noticed that 6 months after they created the website, their overall sales increased dramatically. Following the success of the new website, Topstitch decided to close several of its stores in 2015, since they were making a loss. It also stopped posting printed catalogues out to customers. **Figure 1** shows the sales performance of their high street stores over ten years.

Figure 1

Revenue for Topstitch high street stores between 2007/8 and 2016/7

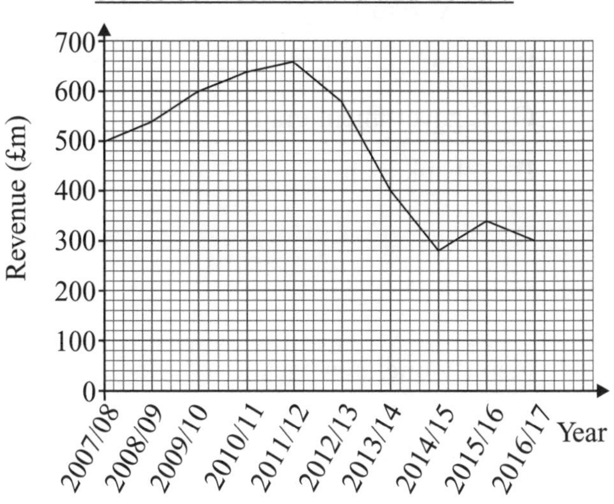

3.1 Explain the trend in revenue for the high street stores between 2011/12 and 2014/15 shown in **Figure 1**. MATHS SKILLS

....

....

[2]

3.2 Analyse what effects the new website may have had on the profits of Topstitch.

....

....

....

....

....

....

....

....

[6]

[Total 8 marks]

Exam Practice Tip

E-commerce is big business nowadays — some companies only sell products online, and chances are you've come across plenty of examples in real life. Make sure you use the evidence that you're given for individual companies, as well as what you already know, when answering questions. If you're given a graph too, chances are you'll need it...

Sources of Finance — Small Firms

1 Which of the following describes a source of finance which doesn't need to be paid back? Shade **one** oval only.

- **A** overdraft ⬭
- **B** trade credit ⬭
- **C** government grant ⬭
- **D** bank loan ⬭

[Total 1 mark]

2 Identify **one** drawback to a business of using each of the following sources of finance.

Trade credit: ....

....

A loan from a friend: ....

....

A government grant: ....

....

[Total 3 marks]

3 James has decided to start a new business — he's going to open a gym in his local area. He decides to buy most of the equipment for his gym using hire purchase.

3.1 Explain how hire purchase works.

....

....

....

[3]

3.2 Buying the equipment using hire purchase is more expensive than if James buys the equipment outright. Explain **one** reason why it still may be advantageous for him to use hire purchase instead.

....

....

....

[3]

[Total 6 marks]

Sources of Finance — Established Firms

Warm-Up

Put the different sources of finance listed on the left into correct column of the table on the right, according to whether or not each source is internal or external.

new share issues

overdrafts

government grants

retained profits

business savings

trade credit

External	Internal

1 Which of the following describes what is meant by retained profits?
Shade **one** oval only.

A Profits which are paid to the shareholders of the business. ⬭

B Money from personal savings. ⬭

C Profits which are invested back into the business. ⬭

D The amount of profit which is paid as tax. ⬭

[Total 1 mark]

2 Explain **one** drawback of using assets as a source of finance.

....

....

[Total 2 marks]

3 A large firm needs to buy 10 new computers for its finance department.

3.1 Explain why issuing shares would not be the best way to finance the new computers.

....

....

....

[3]

3.2 Explain **one** source of finance that would be an appropriate way to finance the new computers.

....

....

[2]

[Total 5 marks]

Investments

1 Look at **Item A** and **Figure 1** below.

Item A — Speedy Wheels:
Speedy Wheels is a courier company that delivers items in parts of the United Kingdom. Speedy Wheels is considering investing £20 000 in new delivery vans. It predicts that these vans will last for approximately five years before they will need to be replaced.

The managers of Speedy Wheels forecast the increase in profit as a result of the new vans in the five years following this investment. Their results are shown in **Figure 1**.

Figure 1

	Year 1	Year 2	Year 3	Year 4	Year 5
additional profit (£000)	17	13	15	15	12

1.1 Identify **two** other investments that could help Speedy Wheels to expand their business.

1. ....

2. ....

[2]

1.2 Use the information above to calculate the average rate of return of the delivery vans. MATHS SKILLS

average rate of return = ...

[4]

1.3 Explain how the predicted average rate of return may affect Speedy Wheels' decision to expand the business. MATHS SKILLS

....

....

....

....

[3]

[Total 9 marks]

Exam Practice Tip

There are a few different steps that you have to remember when calculating the average rate of return on an investment. Make sure you don't miss one of them out — e.g. first you need to calculate the net profit, then divide this by the total number of years you are looking at to find the average annual profit. Then you need to use the equation for ARR.

Break-Even Analysis

1 Which of the following is the correct definition of revenue?
Shade **one** oval only.

A The amount of money a company receives from sales. ⬭

B The amount of money left over after costs are taken into account. ⬭

C The amount of money paid out to shareholders. ⬭

D The total amount of costs over a year. ⬭

[Total 1 mark]

2 A new business makes scarves and sells them for £7. **Figure 1** shows the number of scarves sold by the business in three years and the total costs for each year.

MATHS SKILLS

Figure 1

	Year 1	Year 2	Year 3
Number of scarves sold	850	450	1200
Total revenue	5950	....	....
Total costs (£)	4700	3600	6200

2.1 Complete **Figure 1** to show the total revenue from sales for Years 2 and 3.

[2]

2.2 Explain which year the business made a loss.

....

....

[2]

[Total 4 marks]

3 Explain the difference between fixed and variable costs and give **one** example of each.

....

....

....

....

[Total 4 marks]

4 Ryan is setting up a small business selling mobile phone chargers over the internet. He decides to perform a break-even analysis for the first 6 months of his business. **Figure 2** shows his break-even chart.

Figure 2

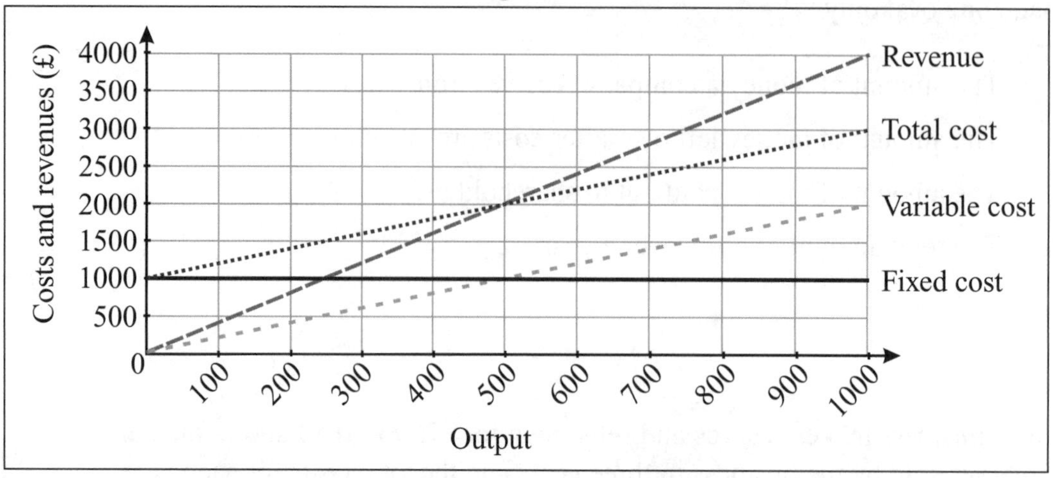

Costs and revenues (£)
4000
3500
3000
2500
2000
1500
1000
500
0
100 200 300 400 500 600 700 800 900 1000
Output
Revenue
Total cost
Variable cost
Fixed cost

4.1 Use **Figure 2** to explain the term 'break-even output'. MATHS SKILLS

....

....

....

[3]

4.2 Ryan predicts that he will sell 800 units in his first 6 months.
Calculate his predicted margin of safety for this period using **Figure 2**. MATHS SKILLS

Margin of safety = ...

[2]

4.3 Analyse the impact of Ryan's break-even analysis on his ability to get a loan.

....

....

....

....

....

....

....

....

[6]

[Total 11 marks]

Exam Practice Tip

Make sure you have a good look at any break-even chart you are given before you try to answer any questions on it. For questions like 4.3 you need to make sure you are relating your answer back to the context in the question — so for this question you should think about how the break-even analysis you are given relates specifically to Ryan's business.

Cash Flow

Warm-Up

Fill in the gaps in the following passage using the correct words from the list below.

buying outflow selling negative net inflow positive paying

A business's cash .... is the amount of money that it receives, for example through .... products. The cash .... is the amount of money it spends, for example, through .... employees. When the .... cash flow is ...., there is more inflow than outflow.

1 Explain why a company might be able to make a profit at the end of a year despite not having positive cash flow throughout the year.

....

....

[Total 2 marks]

2 Tele-wheels Ltd. is a new business selling mobile televisions. **Figure 1** shows a cash flow forecast for Tele-wheels Ltd.

Figure 1

	Jun	Jul	Aug	Sep	Oct	Nov
cash inflow	1500	3000	3200	2700	1700	4000
cash outflow	4000	1500	1750	1410	1500	1660
net cash flow	(2500)	1500	1450	1290	200	2340
bank balance at beginning of month	2000	(500)	1000	2450	3740	3940
bank balance at end of the month	(500)	1000	2450	3740	3940	6280

2.1 Explain **one** reason why it can be useful for a business to perform cash flow forecasts.

....

....

[2]

2.2 Explain which **two** months Tele-wheels Ltd. would need to arrange additional finance for. MATHS SKILLS

....

....

[2]

[Total 4 marks]

3 Yoo Too Sunglasses Ltd. gives its customers 2 months credit to pay.

3.1 **Figure 2** shows the cash flow statement for Yoo Too Sunglasses Ltd.
Complete the statement by filling in the blanks, assuming that all customers make their payment 2 months after their order has been placed. Use the space below for your working.

Figure 2

Cash Flow Statement — Yoo Too Sunglasses Ltd.							
£	Apr	May	Jun	Jul	Aug	Sep	Oct
Total orders this month (for payment in 60 days)	1000	1300	1400	1500	1300	400	300
Cash inflow	300	350	1000	1300	....	1500	1300
Cash outflow	(1000)	1200	1300	....	1250	300	200
Net cash flow	(700)	....	(300)	(50)	150	1200	1100
Opening balance	1300	600	....	(550)	(600)	(450)	750
Closing balance	600	(250)	(550)	(600)	(450)	750	....

[5]

3.2 Explain what is meant by the opening and closing balance on the cash flow statement.

....

....

....

[2]

3.3 There is an unexpected rise in demand for sunglasses in November.
Analyse the impact this may have on Yoo Too Sunglasses Ltd.'s cash flow.

....

....

....

....

....

....

....

....

....

[6]

[Total 13 marks]

Cash Flow — Problems

1 Explain **three** problems which may be caused by poor cash flow in a business.

1. ....

....

2. ....

....

3. ....

....

[Total 6 marks]

2 Look at **Item A** below.

Item A — Shoesies Ltd.:
Shoesies Ltd. is an online company specialising in shoes for children.
It gives customers 30 days' credit on all purchases and also operates a generous returns policy of a full refund on all items returned within 60 days.

Shoesies Ltd. observed that it had falling sales over its final quarter of 2014 and that the number of returns of items had increased.

At the beginning of its financial year in 2015, Shoesies Ltd. had three outstanding loan repayments and a lack of cash in the business. It was also unable to meet its supplier's 10 day credit agreement for purchases of fabrics.

2.1 Explain **two** reasons why Shoesies Ltd. is facing cash flow problems.

1. ....

....

....

2. ....

....

....

[4]

2.2 Shoesies Ltd. is considering two possible ways of solving its cash flow problems:

- Rescheduling their payments.
- Obtaining another source of finance.

Recommend which is the better option for Shoesies Ltd. to take. Give reasons for your advice.
Write your answer on a separate piece of paper.

[9]

[Total 13 marks]

Income Statements

Warm-Up

The list below on the left contains three different components of an income statement. Draw lines to match each component to the sentence describing what it means.

cost of sales	the amount of money left over from the revenue after direct costs are taken into account
gross profit	the amount of money left over from the revenue after all direct and indirect costs are taken into account
operating profit	the amount of money needed to make products

1 Which of the following describes what is meant by the term 'dividends'? Shade **one** oval only.

A Money paid to company executives. ⬭

B Money paid to shareholders. ⬭

C Money used to invest in the business. ⬭

D Money used to pay operating expenses. ⬭

[Total 1 mark]

2 **Figure 1** shows the income statement for Thrill World Ltd., a company which owns theme parks.

2.1 Identify **two** components of the income statement which are **indirect costs** to the business.

....

....

[2]

2.2 In the year ending 31st March 2016, Thrill World Ltd. made a retained profit of £319m. Calculate the percentage change in retained profit between 2015 and 2016. Give your answer to 1 decimal place.

Percentage change = ... %

[2]

[Total 4 marks]

Figure 1

Income Statement
Thrill World Ltd.
Year ending 31st March 2015

		£m
Revenue................................		980
Cost of sales:		
Opening stock........	25	
Purchases..............	200	
	225	
Minus closing stock.......	(76)	
Cost of sales = ...		(149)
Gross profit = ...		831
Minus expenses		
Wages and salaries..	87	
Rent and rates........	46	
Office expenses......	12	
Advertising............	56	
Depreciation...........	102	
Other expenses.......	12	
Expenses = ...		(315)
Operating profit = ...		516
Interest payable		(79)
Profit before tax (Net profit)		437
Taxation		(87.4)
Dividends		(62)
Retained profit		287.6

3 **Figure 2** shows the income statements for Williams' Construction Ltd. for two consecutive years.

Figure 2

Income statement Williams' Construction Ltd. Year ending 31st March 2016		£m
Revenue..............................		713
Cost of sales:		
Opening stock........	45	
Purchases.............	390	
	435	
Minus closing stock........	(75)	
Cost of sales = ...		(360)
Gross profit =.....................		353
Minus expenses		
Wages and salaries..	90	
Rent and rates........	65	
Office expenses......	30	
Advertising.............	12	
Depreciation...........	24	
Other expenses.......	31	
Expenses = ...		(252)
Operating profit = ...		101
Interest payable		(15)
Profit before tax (Net profit)...		86
Taxation		(12.9)
Dividends		(18)
Retained profit		55.1

Income statement Williams' Construction Ltd. Year ending 31st March 2017		£m
Revenue..............................		689
Cost of sales:		
Opening stock........	75	
Purchases.............	320	
	395	
Minus closing stock........	(25)	
Cost of sales = ...		(370)
Gross profit =.....................		319
Minus expenses		
Wages and salaries..	65	
Rent and rates........	45	
Office expenses......	20	
Advertising.............	10	
Depreciation...........	30	
Other expenses.......	24	
Expenses = ...		(194)
Operating profit = ...		125
Interest payable		(15)
Profit before tax (Net profit)..		110
Taxation		(16.5)
Dividends		(18)
Retained profit		75.5

3.1 Explain why investors may be interested in how the operating profit of Williams' Construction Ltd. compares with its gross profit.

....

....

....

[3]

3.2 The company closed several offices and made some staff redundant in April 2016. Analyse the effect that this had on the business's financial performance.

....

....

....

....

....

....

....

....

....

[6]

[Total 9 marks]

Profit Margins

1 Explain what it means if a business has a high gross profit margin but a low net profit margin.

....

....

[Total 2 marks]

2 A catering company has a sales revenue of £3m and a gross profit of £690 000. The cost of its operating expenses (other than cost of sales) and interest are £510 000.

MATHS SKILLS

2.1 Calculate the gross profit margin for the company.

gross profit margin = ...

[2]

2.2 Calculate the net profit margin for the company.

net profit margin = ...

[3]

2.3 A year later, the company calculates its gross profit margin to be 25% and its net profit margin to be 4%. Explain why the company may have decided to find cheaper insurance, based on this information.

....

....

....

[2]

[Total 7 marks]

3 Explain how increasing prices will affect the gross profit margin of a firm if its costs stay the same.

....

....

....

....

....

[Total 4 marks]

Statements of Financial Position

1 Which of the following sentences about statements of financial position is **false**? Shade **one** oval only.

- **A** They show what a business has done with its money. ⬭
- **B** They show whether a business has made a profit or a loss. ⬭
- **C** They show how much debt a business has. ⬭
- **D** They show where a business got its money from. ⬭

[Total 1 mark]

2 Which of the following can be found in the capital employed section of a statement of financial position? Shade **one** oval only.

- **A** value of fixed assets ⬭
- **B** current liabilities ⬭
- **C** net assets ⬭
- **D** value of shareholders' funds ⬭

[Total 1 mark]

3 Explain the difference between current liabilities and long-term liabilities on a statement of financial position, and give examples of both.

....

....

....

....

[Total 4 marks]

4 Established firms have many different sources of finance.

4.1 Explain what is meant by share capital and how shares can be used to raise finance for a firm.

....

....

[2]

4.2 Explain what is meant by retained profits and how they can be used in a business.

....

....

[2]

[Total 4 marks]

5 Explain why the capital employed in a business must always be equal to its net assets.

....

....

....

....

....

[Total 3 marks]

6 Look at **Item A** and **Figure 1** below.

> **Item A — J. Logan:**
> J. Logan is a timber trading company. At the end of November 2016, it had £2850 worth of machinery, a van worth £3500 and £500 in stock. It also owed creditors £200.

6.1 Using examples from **Item A**, explain the difference between assets and liabilities.

....

....

....

....

....

[4]

Figure 1 shows the different sources of finance used by J. Logan.

6.2 What percentage of the total amount of finance is share capital?

MATHS SKILLS

share capital = ...%

[2]

[Total 6 marks]

Figure 1

Sources of finance for J. Logan

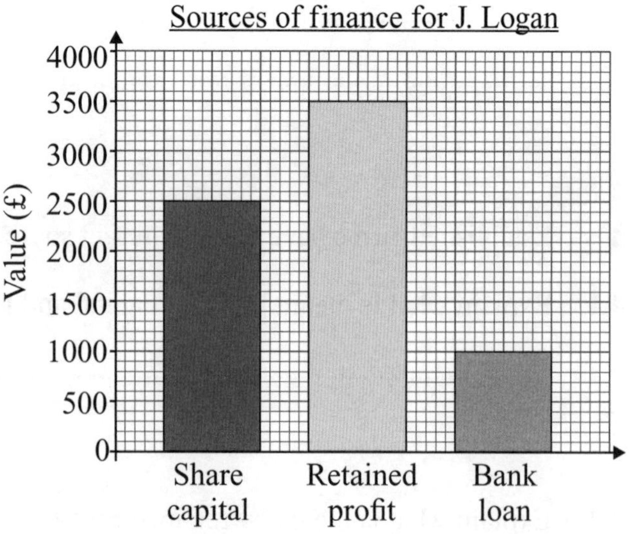

Value (£)

4000
3500
3000
2500
2000
1500
1000
500
0

Share capital
Retained profit
Bank loan

Exam Practice Tip

The information on a statement of financial position is different to the things you'd find on an income statement. Make sure you know what you'd find on each. It'll help if you know your financial terminology through and through.

Analysis — Statements of Financial Position

Warm-Up

Fill in the following passage using the words above it.

capital   internal strengths   financial advisors   liabilities   stakeholders   grants

People who are interested in how well a business is doing are called ....

They may be interested in what sources of .... a business uses to fund itself.

The money that a business borrows and still has to pay back are its ....

1 Which of the following factors could cause a company's fixed assets to fall?
Shade **one** oval only.

A It starts to pay its staff lower wages. ⬭

B It retains less profit. ⬭

C It sells fewer products. ⬭

D It sells some of its property. ⬭

[Total 1 mark]

2 **Figure 1** shows an extract from the statement of financial position for a chain of hairdressers.

Figure 1

Fixed assets	£25500
Current assets	£6950
Current liabilities	£4000
Shareholder capital	£13450
Bank loan	£15000

The business decides to use its cash to invest £3000 in some new equipment. Analyse the impact this might have on how existing shareholders regard the financial performance of the business.

....

....

....

....

....

....

....

....

....

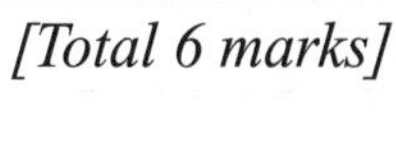

[Total 6 marks]

Analysis — Competitors

1 **Figure 1** shows the statements of financial position for two pizza delivery stores — Lucia's and Pizza Roma.

Figure 1

Lucia's — Statement of Financial Position Dated 31 March 2016	£	£
Fixed Assets:		
Machinery		12000
Van		3200
		15200
Current Assets:		
Stock	3000	
Cash in hand	13000	
	16000	
Current Liabilities:		
Creditors	(9000)	
Bank overdraft	(399)	
	(9399)	
Working Capital:		6601
Net Assets:		21801
Financed by:		
Retained profit		5300
Bank Loan		12000
Net Profit		4501
Capital Employed:		21801

Pizza Roma — Statement of Financial Position Dated 31 March 2016	£	£
Fixed Assets:		
Machinery		17000
Van		6000
		23000
Current Assets:		
Stock	1560	
Cash in hand	5000	
	6560	
Current Liabilities:		
Creditors	(1700)	
Bank overdraft	(60)	
	(1760)	
Working Capital:		4800
Net Assets:		27800
Financed by:		
Retained profit		6600
Bank loan		15000
Net Profit		6200
Capital Employed:		27800

1.1 Explain **one** problem with comparing the financial statements of competitor businesses.

....

....

[2]

1.2 Recommend whether Lucia's should increase their bank loan and pay off their current liabilities in order to help improve their financial performance compared to Pizza Roma.
Give reasons for your answer.
Write your answer on a separate piece of paper.

[9]

[Total 11 marks]

Exam Practice Tip

Sometimes you have to look at every part of a statement of financial position to see where a business is going wrong, or how it can improve. Make sure you don't miss any key bits out. You should also have a really good idea of what you want to write before you start one of these long-answer questions — making a plan first can be handy for that.

Mixed Questions

1 Which of the following happens as part of a price penetration pricing strategy?
Shade **one** oval only.

A A firm charges a very low price for a product when it is new. ⬭
B A firm charges a very high price for a product when it is new. ⬭
C A firm charges a similar price for a product as its competitors are charging. ⬭
D A firm charges a price for a product that is below the cost of making it, even when the product is established in the market. ⬭

[Total 1 mark]

2 Which of the following would help a business to improve their cash flow?
Shade **one** oval only.

A Extending the credit period with their creditors. ⬭
B Buying more raw materials. ⬭
C Extending the credit period with their customers. ⬭
D Paying all bills immediately. ⬭

[Total 1 mark]

3 A caravan retailer sells 45 caravans in a month.
The retailer buys each caravan for £17 000 and sells each one for £20 000.
Which of the following is the retailer's monthly revenue?
Shade **one** oval only.

MATHS SKILLS

A £135 000 ⬭
B £765 000 ⬭
C £900 000 ⬭
D £1 665 000 ⬭

[Total 1 mark]

4 **Figure 1** shows the annual revenue for a business over 5 years.
Calculate the average annual revenue over this time.

MATHS SKILLS

Figure 1

Year	1	2	3	4	5
Revenue (£)	15 000	17 500	16 800	19 300	21 250

average annual revenue = £ ....

[Total 2 marks]

5 Identify **two** methods of organic growth.

....

....

[Total 2 marks]

6 Explain whether using unwanted assets as a source of finance is more suited to new or established businesses.

....

....

....

....

[Total 3 marks]

7 Explain **one** disadvantage of a firm employing staff on zero hour contracts.

....

....

....

....

[Total 3 marks]

8 Explain **one** benefit to a firm of using a just-in-time method of production.

....

....

....

....

[Total 2 marks]

9 Explain **two** reasons why the Equality Act 2010 might increase a firm's costs.

....

....

....

....

....

....

[Total 4 marks]

10 Look at **Item A** below.

Item A — Cut of the Action:
Mel and Paul are two friends who are going to start out in business together. They are going to set up a new, modern hairdressing salon, Cut of the Action, as a partnership. They have seen a premises they want to buy and have a list of hairdressing equipment they will need to get started. They have received an £8000 loan from the bank, but they still need some additional funding. Once the business is up and running, they are planning to promote it by putting adverts in the local newspaper and by sponsoring an annual exhibition at a local art college.

10.1 Explain the difference between the ownership of a sole trader business and of a partnership.

....

....

[2]

10.2 Identify **two** other external sources of finance that Mel and Paul could consider applying for.

....

....

[2]

10.3 Explain **two** factors that may influence Mel and Paul's decision regarding the location of their salon.

....

....

....

....

[4]

10.4 Analyse the suitability of the promotional mix Mel and Paul have chosen.

....

....

....

....

....

....

....

....

....

....

[6]

[Total 14 marks]

11 Look at **Item B** below.

> **Item B — Simpson's Soap Plc.:**
> Simpson's Soap Plc. is a soap manufacturer. In the 12 months up to 31st March 2017, the firm took on 20 new members of staff. Some of these staff were recruited to set up and monitor the firm's social media accounts. The firm also increased its output of soap by 15% and raised its prices slightly. As a result, the company's takings increased by 20%. Despite this increase in revenue, Simpson's profits were down on the previous year, mainly due to the firm's increased staff numbers and its new environmental policy. This policy involves cleaning up pollution in the area around their factory, and trying to use raw materials from more sustainable sources.

11.1 Explain why Simpson's variable costs increased in the 12 months leading up to 31st March 2017.

....

....

[2]

11.2 One of the reasons why Simpson's set up its social media accounts was to provide better customer service. Explain **one** way in which social media can improve customer service.

....

....

[2]

11.3 The National Living Wage was introduced on 1st April 2016.
Explain why this may have influenced Simpson's decision to increase its prices.

....

....

....

....

[3]

11.4 Analyse why there may have been some disagreement between shareholders about Simpson's decision to introduce a new environmental policy.

....

....

....

....

....

....

....

....

[6]

[Total 13 marks]

12 Look at **Item C** and **Figure 2** below.

Item C — Diggitup Ltd.:
Diggitup Ltd. are a company who make gardening equipment. They are based in the UK but they get many of their raw materials from China.

Their best-selling product is the SpadeAce — a tool that can be used as a spade, a fork and a hoe. Before 2007, they only sold the SpadeAce through specialist garden centres to target professional gardeners. In 2007, the SpadeAce was voted as the most popular piece of gardening equipment by professional gardeners.

In 2007, demand for the SpadeAce increased rapidly as more people became interested in growing their own fruit and vegetables. Largely due to this changing trend, in 2007 Diggitup Ltd. saw their revenue grow to £800 000, giving them a net profit of £164 000. To meet the increased demand for the SpadeAce, the company took out a £250 000 loan so that they could buy some new machinery, which would allow them to increase their output. The company also wanted to change their marketing mix to meet the new demand. In 2008, Diggitup Ltd. decided to find new places to sell their products to target people who gardened as a hobby. Diggitup Ltd. looked at the sales figures of a large supermarket chain. The diagrams in **Figure 2** show the sales of non-food products at the supermarket in the years 2005 and 2007.

Due to their success in 2007, Diggitup Ltd. set new aims which focused on growing the business significantly by 2010.

Figure 2

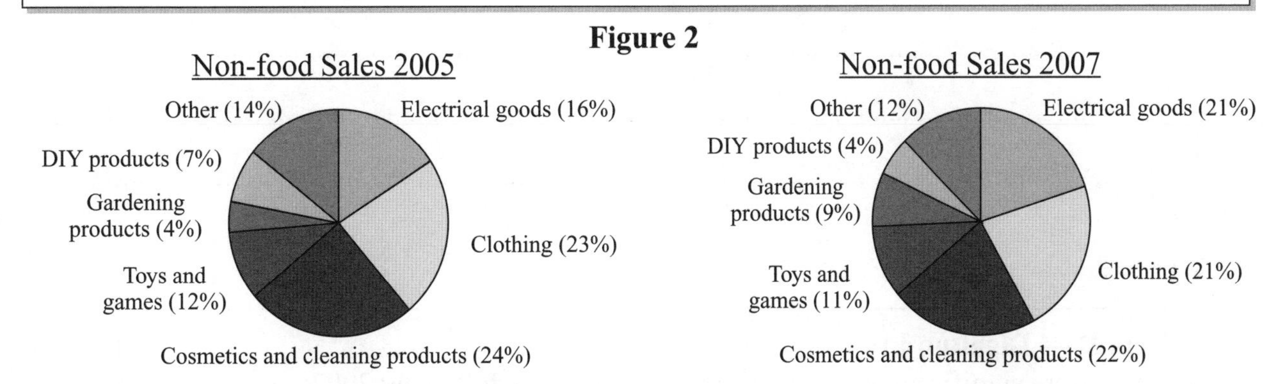

12.1 In 2006, Diggitup Ltd.'s net profit margin was 18.2%.
Calculate the difference in the net profit margin between 2006 and 2007.

MATHS SKILLS

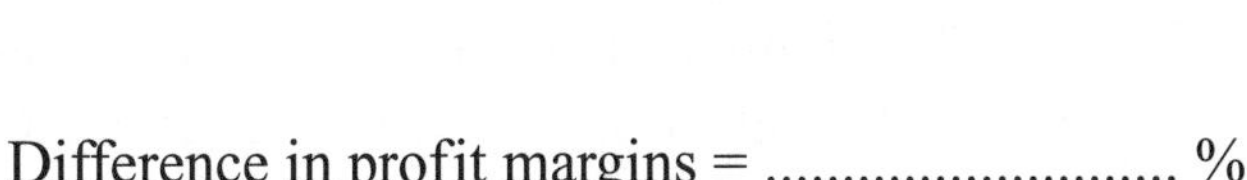

Difference in profit margins = ... %

[3]

12.2 Diggitup Ltd. decided to start selling the SpadeAce at branches of the supermarket.
Using the data in **Figure 2**, explain why they might have made this decision.

MATHS SKILLS

....

....

....

....

....

[3]

12.3 Diggitup Ltd. had considered selling their products via telesales.
Explain **one** reason why the decision to use this channel of distribution may have been rejected.

....

....

....
[2]

12.4 Explain what the SpadeAce is likely to have been called on the Boston Matrix in 2007.

....

....

....

....
[3]

12.5 With the upward trend in people growing their own fruit and vegetables,
Diggitup Ltd. faced more risk from competitors entering the market.
Explain **two** reasons why this may have been costly for the firm.

....

....

....

....

....
[4]

Item D — Diggitup Ltd.:
There were significant economic changes in the years following 2007:

- At the start of 2008, the UK unemployment rate was 5.2%.
  This figure had risen to 7.8% by the end of 2009.
- At the start of 2008, the Bank of England base rate for interest was 5.5%.
  This figure had fallen to 0.5% by the end of 2009.
- At the start of 2008, the exchange rate of the British pound against the Chinese currency, the yuan, was 14.4. This figure had fallen to 11.0 by the end of 2009.

12.6 Analyse the impact of the changing economic climate on Diggitup Ltd.'s plans to grow significantly by 2010. In your answer you should consider:

- consumer spending
- business costs

You must evaluate which area will have the biggest impact on the business.
Use evidence to support your answer.
Write your answer on a separate piece of paper.

[12]
[Total 27 marks]

13 Look at **Item E** below.

Item E — Raymer's Ltd.:
Raymer's Ltd. are a baked-bean manufacturer located on the outskirts of a town in the UK. They use flow production to make their product and employ over 90 staff. The firm's sales have grown each year and the directors have set new objectives for the business which focus on diversification and growth.

Another local food manufacturing company has recently gone bust. Raymer's Ltd. are hoping they can buy this firm's old factory building so they can expand their business. If the expansion goes ahead, Raymer's Ltd. estimate that they will need to increase their workforce by 15%. Many of the new staff will be factory workers — the firm are planning to use on-the-job training to train these staff.

13.1 Identify **two** forms of training Raymer's Ltd. could use to train their new factory workers, other than on-the-job training.

....

....

[2]

13.2 Explain why on-the-job training may be an appropriate form of training for the factory workers.

....

....

....

....

[3]

13.3 Explain why flow production is an appropriate production method for Raymer's Ltd.

....

....

....

[2]

13.4 Raymer's Ltd. considered the opinions of its stakeholders whilst setting its growth objectives. Explain why employees and suppliers are likely to approve of Raymers's Ltd.'s expansion plans.

....

....

....

....

....

[3]

The directors are concerned that the planned expansion may adversely affect the quality of their products.

13.5 Explain **one** way in which the directors may be able to ensure that the quality of their products remains high following the expansion.

....

....

[2]

13.6 Explain **two** reasons why quality may suffer when the firm expands.

....

....

....

....

....

....

[4]

13.7 Raymer's Ltd. will need some new factory supervisors if the expansion goes ahead. They will need to decide whether to recruit internally and train existing factory workers to be supervisors, or to recruit externally.
Recommend which method of recruitment would be best for Raymer's Ltd.
Give reasons for your advice.
Write your answer on a separate piece of paper.

[9]

Item F — Raymer's Ltd.:
Raymer's Ltd. bought the old factory building and went ahead with the expansion.
After the expansion, they steadily increased the output of their products by 30%. The sales team found several new customers including a supermarket chain, for which Raymer's Ltd. agreed to add the supermarket's own labels to the tins. Due to the growth of the firm, Raymer's Ltd. recruited two customer service assistants to deal directly with customer queries.

However, following the expansion, the percentage of products that were returned by customers increased. Common complaints included loose labels, dented tins, and tins that contained a lower weight of produce than was stated on the label.

13.8 Analyse the impact of the expansion on the reputation of the business.
In your answer you should consider:

- customer service
- consumer law

You must evaluate which area would have had the biggest impact on the business.
Use evidence to support your answer.
Write your answer on a separate piece of paper.

[12]

[Total 37 marks]

Answers

Note on Answers:

A lot of the time in Business, there isn't really a "right answer". Instead, it's about being able to explain yourself and justify your decisions.

Page 5 — Why Businesses Exist

Warm-Up

Goods: greengrocers, furniture shop, online clothes store
Services: taxi firm, dentist, cinema, accountancy firm

1 A ***[1 mark]***

2 Needs are goods or services you can't live without ***[1 mark]***. For example, water / food ***[1 mark]***. Wants are goods or services you would like to have but can survive without ***[1 mark]***. For example, a holiday / jewellery ***[1 mark]***.

3 The primary sector produces raw materials ***[1 mark]***. The farm is part of this sector because it produces milk, which is a raw material ***[1 mark]***. The secondary sector manufactures goods ***[1 mark]***. The farm is part of this sector because it manufactures ice cream ***[1 mark]***.

Page 6 — Enterprise

1 B ***[1 mark]***

2.1 Hint: there are many reasons you could give here, e.g. she may have wanted to be her own boss, she may have been dissatisfied with her current job, she may have wanted more flexible working hours, etc. For whatever reason you give, make sure you explain it using information from Item A.
E.g. Bushra identified a gap in the market ***[1 mark]***, as she discovered that people would be willing to buy fashionable, vegan-friendly and ethically produced shoes, and that there weren't any companies that produced shoes like these ***[1 mark]***.

2.2 E.g. an entrepreneur is someone who takes on the risks of enterprise activity ***[1 mark]***. Bushra has done this by starting up a business ***[1 mark]***.

2.3 How to grade your answer:
Level 0: Nothing worthy of credit. ***[No marks]***
Level 1: There is some attempt to state the qualities that Bushra has shown, but there is little or no explanation to back up these statements. ***[1 to 2 marks]***
Level 2: There is a basic analysis of the qualities that Bushra has shown, but the explanations are lacking in detail, or points have been missed. ***[3 to 4 marks]***
Level 3: There is a thorough analysis of the qualities that Bushra has shown, with detailed explanations of how she has shown them. ***[5 to 6 marks]***
Here are some points your answer may include:
Bushra has quit her job as a journalist to start her own company. This shows that she is willing to take risks.
Bushra has identified a gap in the market for fashionable, vegan-friendly and ethically produced shoes. This shows that she is innovative.
Bushra has made sure the manufacturers provide her with quantities of stock that she's able to store in her office. She's also prepared a successful presentation to a nationwide retail firm. This shows that she is organised.
Bushra has worked hard to find the right manufacturer for her shoes, by visiting many trade shows. She also worked hard before the presentation to the nationwide retail store, as she didn't take a day off for two weeks. This shows that she is hardworking.

Page 7 — Factors of Production

1 Land: e.g. land is territory and all of Earth's natural resources ***[1 mark]***. For example, gas / oil / coal /wind power / tidal power / wood / diamonds / gold / water / animals ***[1 mark]***.
Capital: e.g. capital is things that are needed to help produce goods and services but have to be made first ***[1 mark]***. For example, equipment / factories / schools ***[1 mark]***.

2.1 Dirk has limited labour ***[1 mark]***, as he is the only person who is able to make the bouquets and he doesn't have time to complete both orders ***[1 mark]***.

2.2 Opportunity cost is the benefit that's given up in order to do something else ***[1 mark]***. In Dirk's case, he has given up the opportunity of supplying the wedding magazine in order to supply the stately home ***[1 mark]***. The opportunity cost of this decision is the £600 he would have made from supplying the wedding magazine and any extra business that would have been generated from having his business's name printed in the magazine ***[1 mark]***.

Pages 8-10 — Business Ownership Structures

Warm-Up

1 true 2 true 3 false 4 false

1 B ***[1 mark]***

2 Hint: there are four marks here — two marks for giving two disadvantages, and two marks for explaining the impact each disadvantage could have.
Any two from: e.g. sole traders may have to work long hours / not get many holidays ***[1 mark]***, so they may regularly feel tired ***[1 mark]***. / Sole traders have unlimited liability ***[1 mark]***, which means if the business goes bust they are legally responsible for paying back all of the business's debts ***[1 mark]***. / Sole traders are also unincorporated ***[1 mark]***, so if anyone sues the business, the sole trader is sued personally ***[1 mark]***. / It can be hard for a sole trader to raise money ***[1 mark]***, so it may be hard to grow the business ***[1 mark]***.

3 E.g. in a private limited company, all the shareholders have to agree before any shares are sold ***[1 mark]***. This means that the owners keep control of who has a say in managing the business ***[1 mark]***. A private limited company has limited liability ***[1 mark]***. This reduces the financial risks for the owners as it means they won't lose more money than they've invested if the business goes bust ***[1 mark]***.

4 E.g. private limited companies are expensive to set up because of all the legal paperwork that must be done ***[1 mark]***, and the partnership may not be able to afford this ***[1 mark]***. Private limited companies are legally obliged to publish their accounts every year ***[1 mark]***, which may mean extra work for the partnership that they don't want to commit to ***[1 mark]***.

5.1 A not-for-profit business is one which generates enough income to cover its costs ***[1 mark]*** but puts any surplus back into the business / uses any surplus to fund projects that help the community ***[1 mark]***.

5.2 E.g. the separate companies won't have the same restrictions on what they can sell as the National Trust as they're not charities ***[1 mark]***, so the National Trust can use these companies to generate extra income ***[1 mark]***.

5.3 E.g. being incorporated means the people who run the National Trust have limited liability ***[1 mark]***, so they're not responsible for all of the National Trust's debts if it goes bust ***[1 mark]*** and aren't personally liable if the National Trust is sued ***[1 mark]***.

6 How to grade your answer:

Level 0: Nothing worthy of credit. ***[No marks]***

Level 1: There is some attempt to describe the effect of Blackwell's Pies becoming a public limited company, but with little explanation of how these changes may affect the Blackwell family. ***[1 to 2 marks]***

Level 2: The effects of Blackwell's Pies becoming a public limited company have been described, with some explanation of how these changes could affect the Blackwell family. ***[3 to 4 marks]***

Level 3: There is a detailed description of the effects of Blackwell's Pies becoming a public limited company, and a clear explanation of how these differences could affect the Blackwell family. ***[5 to 6 marks]***

Here are some points your answer may include:

Converting the company to a PLC means that the company will be able to raise much more capital through selling shares on the stock exchange, which would help it to expand further. Expansion may mean that the company makes more profit, which could lead to higher dividends for the Blackwell family.

Converting to a PLC would make it possible for somebody to buy enough shares to take over the company, meaning the Blackwell family could end up losing overall control.

Converting to a PLC would mean there are more shareholders, so the Blackwell family would lose some control over deciding the aims of the business in the future.

Becoming a PLC would mean more shareholders, so each member of the Blackwell family would get a smaller share of the profits than before.

7.1 A partnership is made up of two or more people ***[1 mark]***. Each partner has an equal say in all business decisions ***[1 mark]*** and receives an equal share of the profits (unless they have agreed otherwise) ***[1 mark]***.

7.2 How to grade your answer:

Level 0: Nothing worthy of credit. ***[No marks]***

Level 1: Some attempt has been made to recommend what Kate should do, but with little explanation for why this should be done. ***[1 to 3 marks]***

Level 2: Some of the advantages and disadvantages of Kate going into partnership have been described, along with a recommendation of what she should do. There is some reasoning to the recommendation, but it is lacking in detail or not fully explained. ***[4 to 6 marks]***

Level 3: There is a detailed explanation of the advantages and disadvantages of going into business with a partner, with a well-reasoned and fully explained recommendation of what Kate should do. ***[7 to 9 marks]***

Here are some points your answer may include:

Advantages of partnership

Kate does not have a lot of money to put into the business. Starting up with a partner will mean that there is more capital available to start the business than if she started as a sole trader.

Kate has only just qualified as an accountant. Having a partner could mean there's a broader range of skills and expertise, which could be useful for Kate as she starts her career.

Kate and her partner would be able to share work, so it would reduce the workload for Kate compared to starting a business as a sole trader.

Disadvantages of partnership

Kate would be legally responsible for the actions of the other person in the partnership, and as Kate doesn't know this person very well, this could be very risky.

The partner Kate is considering might not want to run the business in the same way as Kate. There could be disagreements if they have very different ideas about how the business should be run.

Having a partner means Kate will get a smaller share of the profits compared to if she was a sole trader.

Make sure you finish your answer with a conclusion recommending what you think Kate should do — it doesn't matter which you choose as long as you give reasons. E.g. 'Kate should start up as a sole trader. Even though this means she may have to work longer hours, and have less money to start with, it means that she doesn't have the risks of working with someone she doesn't know very well, and will earn a greater share of the profits.'

Pages 11-12 — Business Aims and Objectives

1 Aims are overall goals that a business wants to achieve ***[1 mark]***. Objectives are more specific targets ***[1 mark]*** which are used to help measure how well a business is achieving its aims ***[1 mark]***.

2.1 Any two from: e.g. to increase income from sales / to have high customer satisfaction / to increase the number of employees ***[2 marks — 1 mark for each correct answer]***.

2.2 How to grade your answer:

Level 0: Nothing worthy of credit. ***[No marks]***

Level 1: There is a basic description of how Karen's aims might have changed, but with little explanation of why Rye Ltd. may have caused these changes. ***[1 to 2 marks]***

Level 2: There is a detailed description of how Karen's aims might have changed, with a detailed explanation of why Rye Ltd. might have caused these changes. ***[3 to 4 marks]***

Here is an answer you could have written:

Karen may have to change her aims to focus more on maintaining her market share. This is because Rye Ltd. is a direct competitor of Karen's Sarnies. It is a large, national company meaning it is likely to have a well established brand, so is likely to take lots of customers from Karen.

2.3 Rye Ltd. is a much bigger and more established company than Karen's Sarnies ***[1 mark]***, so its aims are likely to be focused on things which require a lot of money / brand recognition ***[1 mark]***. E.g. one of Rye Ltd.'s aims might be to dominate the sandwich retail market ***[1 mark]***.

3.1 E.g. Ole could have set himself yearly sales targets ***[1 mark]***, increasing to over £1m by the end of the fifth year ***[1 mark]***. These would have acted as measurable steps to check he was on track for achieving his aim ***[1 mark]***.

3.2 How to grade your answer:
Level 0: Nothing worthy of credit. ***[No marks]***
Level 1: There is some attempt to state how successful Ole was at achieving two of his aims, but there is little or no explanation to back up conclusions. ***[1 to 2 marks]***
Level 2: There is a basic analysis of how successful Ole was at achieving two of his aims, but the explanations are lacking in detail, or points have been missed. ***[3 to 4 marks]***
Level 3: There is a thorough analysis of how successful Ole was at achieving two of his aims, with detailed explanations of how successful he was. ***[5 to 6 marks]***
Here are some points your answer may include:
Aim 1
Ole aimed to make a profit in the first five years.
The graph shows that in the fifth year, Ole made a small loss.
Whilst Ole didn't achieve his aim in the fifth year, he was close, as previously he had been losing at least £100 000 each year. He also managed to make a profit of £200 000 the following year, so only narrowly missed being successful in achieving this aim.
Aim 2
Ole had an aim to have sales of over £1m per year by the fifth year.
In fact, after five years, Ole only had sales of £500 000, and didn't achieve sales of £1m until eight years after opening, so he didn't succeed in achieving this aim.
Aim 3
Ole had an aim to become a nationally recognised company after eight years.
In the sixth year after opening, Ole started advertising nationally, so would have started to be recognised throughout the country.
In the seventh year after opening, a national department store started stocking Ole's products, which would have raised his national profile further.
Overall, Ole was successful in making his company nationally recognised after eight years.

Page 13 — Stakeholders

1.1 E.g. customers will want lower prices ***[1 mark]***, and Better Energy Plc. have satisfied this objective by lowering the cost of their energy ***[1 mark]***. Some customers may want companies to have a smaller impact on the environment ***[1 mark]***, which Better Energy Plc. have done by investing in renewable energy ***[1 mark]***.
1.2 How to grade your answer:
Level 0: Nothing worthy of credit. ***[No marks]***
Level 1: There is a basic description of some likely impacts to stakeholders, but with little explanation of why the actions of Better Energy Plc. may cause these impacts. ***[1 to 3 marks]***
Level 2: There is a basic explanation of some of the impacts that Better Energy Plc.'s actions will have on the stakeholders. There is some attempt to conclude which stakeholder will have a greater influence on the business, but with little or no explanation to justify the conclusion. ***[4 to 6 marks]***
Level 3: There is a good description of how Better Energy Plc.'s actions will influence its stakeholders. There is a conclusion as to which stakeholder will have a greater influence on the business, but the justification is lacking in detail. ***[7 to 9 marks]***
Level 4: There is a detailed and thorough analysis of how Better Energy Plc.'s actions will influence its stakeholders. A conclusion has been made as to which stakeholder will have a greater influence on the business, which has been fully justified using evidence. ***[10 to 12 marks]***
Here are some points your answer may include:
Impact on the residents of Madingborough
The project involves investing in local roads, so could benefit local residents as their transport links would be improved.
A local community can suffer if a business causes noise and pollution.
Many of the local residents are employed in the local tourism industry. If the wind farm is built near Madingborough, it could spoil the Area of Outstanding Natural Beauty, and mean fewer tourists go to the area. So the tourism industry, and people employed by it, may suffer.
Impact on shareholders
Shareholders will often want a business to maximise its profits so they get high dividends.
The site near Madingborough is cheaper than building offshore, so the shareholder's dividends would be less affected.
The site near Madingborough would take less time to build. This means that the company could start selling electricity sooner, meaning shareholders could also see their dividends increasing sooner.
The protests about the site near Madingborough have gained the attention of media and minor celebrities. If the site gets too much negative press, shareholders might get concerned that the business may start losing customers and that their share price might fall, so shareholders might start selling their shares.
Make sure you finish your answer with a conclusion about which stakeholder will have the most influence over the decision Better Energy Plc. make — it doesn't matter which stakeholder you choose as long as you justify your reasons. E.g. 'The local residents will have the biggest influence on whether Better Energy Plc. build their wind farm in Madingborough. They have created negative press for the company which may influence how other stakeholders, such as the shareholders, view the business, and this could damage Better Energy Plc.'s revenue and profits more than if they invested in the more expensive wind farm.'

Page 14 — Revenue, Costs and Profit

Warm-Up
insurance, rent and managers' salaries.
1.1 The variable costs increased from £30 000 in 2015 to £40 000 in 2016 ***[1 mark]*** because they depend on output, and the output of the business increased during this period ***[1 mark]***. The fixed costs were the same (£40 000) in both 2015 and 2016 ***[1 mark]*** because they don't vary with output ***[1 mark]***.
1.2 average unit cost = total cost ÷ output ***[1 mark]***
total cost = fixed costs + variable costs
= 40 000 + 40 000 = £80 000
average unit cost = 80 000 ÷ 12 500 = **£6.40** ***[2 marks for correct answer, otherwise 1 mark for correctly calculating total cost]***

1.3 profit = revenue – costs
profit in 2015 = 90 000 – 30 000 – 40 000 = £20 000
profit in 2016 = 110 000 – 40 000 – 40 000 = £30 000
change in profit = 30 000 – 20 000 = £10 000
Percentage increase = (10 000 ÷ 20 000) × 100 = **50%**
[4 marks for correct answer, otherwise 1 mark for correctly calculating profit in 2015, 1 mark for correctly calculating profit in 2016, 1 mark for correctly calculating change in profit]

Page 15 — The Business Plan

1 A ***[1 mark]***

2.1 Hint: your answer should include a brief description of one reason why writing a business plan is a good idea, and an explanation of how this will benefit Sam's business. You get one mark for the reason, and one mark for the explanation.
E.g. the plan can be used to convince the bank that the business is a sound investment ***[1 mark]***, so would help Sam to get the money he needs to start the business ***[1 mark]***. / The plan will force Sam to think carefully about what the business is going to do / how it's going to be organised / what resources it will need ***[1 mark]***, so will help him work out how much money he will need to borrow ***[1 mark]***.

2.2 Hint: for the problems you describe, make sure you explain how they could affect Sam's business.
E.g. if Sam was too optimistic in predicting that the business will grow 60% each year ***[1 mark]***, he could end up with problems later on, such as struggling to pay his bills if he doesn't make as much money as he's expecting ***[1 mark]***. There may also be changes in the business environment that Sam hadn't accounted for in his business plan, such as a competitor entering the market ***[1 mark]***, and if he doesn't change his plan in response, the business could suffer ***[1 mark]***.

Page 16 — Location

1 B ***[1 mark]***

A hairdresser will want to be somewhere that its customers can easily get to. The other companies sell over the internet or phone, or deliver nationally, so being near their customers will be less important.

2 Hint: for the reason you choose, make sure you explain why it would benefit the business. You get one mark for the reason, and one mark for the explanation.
E.g. if the company sells products across the world, it might choose to set up a site in a country where it has a large market ***[1 mark]***. This would reduce transport costs to the country / means the business wouldn't have to pay import taxes in that country ***[1 mark]***. / Labour costs may be cheaper abroad compared to in the UK ***[1 mark]***, meaning that the company's costs would be lower and it may be able to make more profit ***[1 mark]***.

3.1 E.g. Hampton is an area of high unemployment ***[1 mark]***, so wages may be low / there'll be a good selection of people to choose from to employ / there'll be enough people to fill all the jobs in the new factory / there may be grants or tax breaks available ***[1 mark]***.

3.2 How to grade your answer:
Level 0: Nothing worthy of credit. ***[No marks]***
Level 1: Some attempt has been made to recommend what DP Oak Ltd. should do, but with little explanation for why this is the best option. ***[1 to 3 marks]***
Level 2: Some of the advantages and disadvantages of each option have been described, along with a recommendation of which option DP Oak Ltd. should choose. There is some reasoning to the recommendation, but it is lacking in detail or not fully explained. ***[4 to 6 marks]***
Level 3: There is a detailed explanation of the advantages and disadvantages of each option, with a well-reasoned and fully explained recommendation of what DP Oak Ltd. should do. ***[7 to 9 marks]***

Here are some points your answer may include:

Site 1

The rent is cheaper at Site 1, which would reduce DP Oak Ltd.'s fixed costs.
Site 1 is close to a wood-processing plant, so transport costs associated with obtaining the raw materials needed to make the wardrobes are likely to be lower.
Site 1 is located 10 miles out of town, but this shouldn't affect sales as DP Oak Ltd. sell their products online, so locating close to the market isn't a high priority.
However, being further away from the town may mean that it is more difficult for staff to get to work, which may make it harder for DP Oak Ltd. to recruit enough staff.

Site 2

Site 2 is more expensive than Site 1, so DP Oak Ltd.'s fixed costs would be higher.
Site 2 is located near a college, which could be convenient for staff if they need training in the skills needed to make the wardrobes.
Site 2 is on a bus route, so it might be easier to recruit people as they'll be able to get to work more easily.

Make sure you finish your answer with a conclusion recommending which site you think would be best for the new factory — it doesn't matter which you choose as long as you give reasons. E.g. 'Site 1 would be the best option. Even though it may be more difficult to hire employees at this site, the benefits of cheaper rent and cheaper transport costs are likely to outweigh this in the long term.'

Page 17 — Expanding Businesses

1 C ***[1 mark]***

2.1 E.g. a diseconomy of scale occurs when the growth of a firm leads to an increase in the average unit cost of the firm's products ***[1 mark]***. After expanding, VDP saw the productivity of its staff go down, which could have increased its average unit costs ***[1 mark]***. This could have been because the increase in staff numbers made communication more difficult / made workers feel demotivated / made business activities difficult to coordinate ***[1 mark]***.

2.2 How to grade your answer:
Level 0: Nothing worthy of credit. ***[No marks]***
Level 1: There is an attempt to explain how expansion may have affected revenue or costs, with some attempt to link this to profit. ***[1 to 2 marks]***
Level 2: The likely effects on profit have been described, with some explanation of why the profits would have changed. ***[3 to 4 marks]***
Level 3: There is a detailed description of how the expansion may have affected VDP's profits over the course of the first two years, and a clear explanation of why the profits would have changed in this way. ***[5 to 6 marks]***

Here are some points your answer may include:
In the first year, VDP suffered from a diseconomy of scale due to the workforce becoming less productive.
They would have also had higher costs as they had more staff to pay and a larger building to run.
These things would have caused average unit costs to increase, so profits are also likely to have fallen.
After two years, productivity was back to the same level as before the expansion.
This means VDP would have started to benefit from economies of scale caused by the expansion. For example, even though the call centre doubled in size, it wouldn't have been twice as expensive to run, so the average unit costs of the call centre should have gone down.
After two years, average weekly revenue had increased by 40%. This, combined with the economy of scale from the larger building should have meant that VDP was making more profit on its revenue. So after two years profits should have increased.

Page 18 — Internal Expansion

Warm-Up
outsourcing — When a company pays another firm to carry out tasks that it could do itself.
e-commerce — When a company sells products via the internet.
franchising — When a company gives other firms the right to sell its products or use its name, in return for a fee or a share of the profits.

1 Hint: to get all the marks here, you need to clearly state a benefit and drawback of expanding using e-commerce, and explain how Purrfect Catz Ltd. could be affected by each of these things.
E.g. selling products via the internet means that the business has access to a much larger market ***[1 mark]***, so its sales are likely to increase ***[1 mark]***. However, if the website has any technical problems, customers could become dissatisfied ***[1 mark]***, and Purrfect Catz Ltd.'s sales could drop ***[1 mark]***.

2 How to grade your answer:
Level 0: Nothing worthy of credit. ***[No marks]***
Level 1: Some attempt has been made to recommend what Harry should do, but with little explanation for why this is the better option. ***[1 to 3 marks]***
Level 2: Some of the advantages and disadvantages of each option have been given, along with a recommendation of which option Harry should choose. There is some reasoning to the recommendation, but it is lacking in detail or not fully explained. ***[4 to 6 marks]***
Level 3: There is a detailed explanation of the advantages and disadvantages of each option, with a well-reasoned and fully explained recommendation of what Harry should do. ***[7 to 9 marks]***
Here are some points your answer may include:
Opening a new shop
If the new shop operates in a similar way to the existing shops, it should be a success, so the business's sales should increase.
Gordale sounds like a good place for Harry's new shop, as the residents are well-paid, sporty and the town is near a national cycle path. These factors suggest that there's likely to be interest in a bicycle shop, so the shop should get a lot of customers.
The cost of rent for a shop in Gordale is higher than the rent for Harry's current shops. If Harry is unable to cover the new extra costs of higher rent and more staff, the expansion could fail and the whole business could lose money, which could put Harry's current shops under threat.
Franchising
Allowing Cathy to open a franchise of Chain Reaction means that Harry's income will increase, as Cathy will pay Harry to run a shop under his brand name.
Franchising means Harry won't have the risks of running a new shop, so if the new shop fails, Harry's other shops shouldn't be affected.
However, franchising means that Harry will get less of any profit from the new shop compared to opening a new shop himself.
Also, Harry doesn't know Cathy, so doesn't know if she has the same standards as him. If Cathy doesn't run the business well, all of Harry's shops could get a bad reputation, which could harm his sales.
Make sure you finish your answer with a conclusion recommending which option you think would be better — it doesn't matter which you choose as long as you give reasons. E.g. 'Harry should open the new shop himself, rather than franchising. Even though the rent is significantly higher, the area he's chosen means the shop should be a success, and his sales have been increasing so he should be able to cover the initial start-up costs. This is a less risky option than franchising to someone he doesn't know, who could harm the reputation of his brand.'

Page 19 — External Expansion

1 D ***[1 mark]***
2.1 E.g. by taking over a supplier, Relish the Day will be able to control the supply/cost/quality of its fruit and vegetables ***[1 mark]***, so its costs may go down / quality may go up ***[1 mark]***.
2.2 How to grade your answer:
Level 0: Nothing worthy of credit. ***[No marks]***
Level 1: Some attempt to describe how takeovers can affect staff morale, but with little explanation of why the staff at Bailes Farming Ltd. would have been affected. ***[1 to 2 marks]***
Level 2: There is a good description of how the takeover may have affected staff morale, with some explanation of why this would have happened. ***[3 to 4 marks]***
Level 3: There is a detailed description of how the takeover may have affected staff morale at Bailes Farming Ltd., and a clear explanation of why this would have happened. ***[5 to 6 marks]***
Here are some points your answer may include:
Before the takeover, Bailes Farming Ltd. was on the brink of closure, so staff morale is likely to have been low as all the employees were at risk of losing their jobs.
However, the takeover meant that Bailes Farming Ltd. didn't close, so not all the employees lost their jobs. This may have caused staff morale to increase.
After the takeover, some of the employees from Bailes Farming Ltd. were made redundant.
This could have caused uncertainty or resentment with the remaining employees, causing staff morale to drop.
Some employees from Relish the Day were moved into management positions at Bailes Farming Ltd.
This could have caused resentment from any employees at Bailes Farming Ltd. who were in line for a promotion to management positions before the takeover.

The employees from Bailes Farming Ltd. may not be motivated by the management style of the managers from Relish the Day, which could cause staff morale to go down. The company's profits have grown since the takeover, which may cause morale to increase if employees benefit from this growth with things such as bonuses or improved working conditions.
Growth also shows that the takeover has been a success, so morale may increase as employees will feel more confident that their jobs aren't at risk.

Page 20 — Employment and the Law

1 D ***[1 mark]***

2.1 Any three from: e.g. carry out risk assessments to identify possible dangers ***[1 mark]***. Take steps to reduce risks to employees ***[1 mark]***. Give staff health and safety training ***[1 mark]***. / Give staff safety equipment ***[1 mark]***.

2.2 E.g. it could be expensive for a business ***[1 mark]***, because they will have to provide training to staff / safety equipment ***[1 mark]***.

2.3 Any two from: e.g. they may be prosecuted / fined / closed down. / They may have to pay compensation. / They may get bad publicity. ***[2 marks — 1 mark for each correct answer]***

3 Advantage: by having a minimum wage, staff are more likely to be motivated ***[1 mark]*** and therefore may be more productive for a business ***[1 mark]***.
Disadvantage: businesses may have increased costs ***[1 mark]***, which may mean that their profit is reduced ***[1 mark]***.

Page 21 — Consumer Law

1.1 money back ***[1 mark]***, a repair ***[1 mark]***, a replacement ***[1 mark]***

1.2 Hint: as well as giving two different ways in which a business may be damaged by breaking consumer law, you also need to make sure you explain both of your suggestions. Each suggestion is worth one mark and each explanation is also worth one mark.
Any two from: e.g. it may have to give a refund, replace or repair the faulty products ***[1 mark]***, which will cost the business money ***[1 mark]***. / It may have to defend itself in court ***[1 mark]***, which would cost money ***[1 mark]***. / The reputation of the business may be damaged ***[1 mark]***, which could lead to a drop in sales ***[1 mark]***.

2.1 If the DVD doesn't play through then it's not of satisfactory quality to meet consumer law ***[1 mark]***. If the DVD doesn't match its case then it's a false trade description and so doesn't meet consumer law ***[1 mark]***.

2.2 Any two from: e.g. he shouldn't sell any DVDs that do not play properly ***[1 mark]***. / For any DVDs that are in the wrong DVD case he should repackage them so that the packaging correctly describes the DVD inside ***[1 mark]***.

Page 22 — Technology and Business

1 Any three from: e.g. social media / websites / email / mobile apps / live chats / video calls ***[3 marks — 1 mark for each correct answer]***

2 E.g. using digital communication is often faster/easier ***[1 mark]*** and ensures that businesses stay competitive ***[1 mark]***.

3.1 E.g. it allows Amazon® to reach a wider market ***[1 mark]***, since people will be able to buy products from the website anywhere in the world ***[1 mark]***.

3.2 E.g. it is expensive ***[1 mark]***. They have had to employ new staff to manage the robotics system ***[1 mark]***.

3.3 Any two from: e.g. it allows them to locate products more quickly ***[1 mark]***. / It allows them to keep track of products more easily ***[1 mark]***. / It means that the company is more productive ***[1 mark]***.

Page 23 — Ethical Considerations

1.1 E.g. so that the company acts in ways that the stakeholders think are fair ***[1 mark]*** and honest ***[1 mark]***.

1.2 Any two from: e.g. ensuring that it rewards its staff fairly ***[1 mark]***. / Ensuring that it keeps personal details of staff private ***[1 mark]***. / Ensuring that it provides a comfortable working environment ***[1 mark]***.

1.3 Any two from: e.g. using non-toxic materials ***[1 mark]***. / Paying close attention to safety ***[1 mark]***. / Not using animal testing ***[1 mark]***.

2 How to grade your answer:
Level 0: Nothing worthy of credit. ***[No marks]***
Level 1: There is some attempt to state the effects of using Fair Trade products on the financial success of Beancraft Ltd., but there is little or no explanation of the causes of these effects. ***[1 to 2 marks]***
Level 2: There is a basic analysis of how using Fair Trade products might affect the financial success of Beancraft Ltd., but the explanations are lacking in detail, or points have been missed. ***[3 to 4 marks]***
Level 3: There is a thorough analysis of how using Fair Trade products might affect the financial success of Beancraft Ltd., with detailed explanations of the causes of these effects. ***[5 to 6 marks]***
Here are some points your answer may include:
Workers on coffee bean plantations that are Fair Trade certified will get a fair wage, which will allow them to afford a better quality of life. However, buying only from Fair Trade certified plantations may mean that Beancraft Ltd. will have to pay more for coffee beans than its competitors.
This could mean that the prices of its coffee products are higher than those of its competitors. This may mean that consumers choose its competitors' coffee instead of Beancraft Ltd.'s, leading to a loss in revenue.
Beancraft Ltd. will also have a smaller selection of plantations to buy from than its competitors, since a smaller number of plantations are Fair Trade certified than those that are not. This may mean that it won't be able to offer varieties of coffee that its competitors offer, which may mean that customers won't choose its products and it will have a loss in revenue.
However, Beancraft Ltd. may be able to include details of its use of Fair Trade sources of coffee beans in its marketing, in order to emphasise the company's ethical principles. Most of its competitors do not use Fair Trade sources of coffee beans, so emphasising the use of Fair Trade sources in Beancraft Ltd.'s marketing could help it to stand out from its competition. This may mean that customers who want to buy ethical products will choose Beancraft Ltd.'s coffee over its competitors'. This will lead to an increase in revenue for Beancraft Ltd.

Page 24 — Environmental Influences

Warm-Up

sustainability, renewable, warming

1.1 Any two from: e.g. They could package products more efficiently ***[1 mark]***, so that fewer van journeys are needed to transport products, leading to less pollution ***[1 mark]***. / They could reduce the amount of packaging on products ***[1 mark]***, so that they are using fewer resources ***[1 mark]***. / They could use machinery which is quieter/more efficient ***[1 mark]*** to reduce noise/air pollution ***[1 mark]***.

1.2 E.g. it could improve the image of ForKids ***[1 mark]*** which will attract new customers / increase sales ***[1 mark]***.

1.3 E.g. it may be expensive ***[1 mark]*** because new equipment / new processes will be needed ***[1 mark]***.

Page 25 — Unemployment and Consumer Spending

1 E.g. it may mean that people have less money to spend ***[1 mark]***. This could mean that there is less demand for and fewer sales of the products or services offered by the business ***[1 mark]***.

2 E.g. if a person has been out of work for a long time, they may have lost the skills needed to do the job ***[1 mark]***, so the business would have to spend money retraining them ***[1 mark]***.

3 E.g. between 2006 and 2017 both the consumer price index and average weekly wage increased in country A ***[1 mark]***, but the average weekly income increased by a smaller amount than the consumer price index (the price of goods) ***[1 mark]***. Therefore, a typical consumer won't have as much money available to spend on luxury items ***[1 mark]***, so demand for and therefore sales of these items may decrease ***[1 mark]***.

Page 26 — Interest Rates

1 B ***[1 mark]***

High interest rates mean that borrowing is more expensive. So the banks that loan money will earn more from interest.

2.1 1984 ***[1 mark]*** because this is the year in which interest rates were at their highest ***[1 mark]***.

2.2 Interest rates decreased overall between 1980 and 2010 ***[1 mark]***. When interest rates decrease, borrowing becomes cheaper (and saving money less beneficial) ***[1 mark]***, so there would have been increased consumer spending ***[1 mark]***, which may have led to increased business profits ***[1 mark]***.

Page 27 — Competition

Warm-Up

true, false, true, true

1.1 At first competition in the portable baby bath market was low / there was no competition ***[1 mark]*** because Travel Bath was the only product available ***[1 mark]***. Then over time, competition increased ***[1 mark]*** as other companies brought similar products onto the market ***[1 mark]***.

1.2 How to grade your answer:

Level 0: Nothing written worthy of credit. ***[No marks]***

Level 1: Some attempt has been made to recommend what Bluebell Babies should do, but with little explanation for why this should be done. ***[1 to 3 marks]***

Level 2: Some of the advantages and disadvantages of Bluebell Babies reducing the price of Travel Bath and investing in new marketing material have been given, along with a recommendation for what they should do. There is some reasoning to the recommendation, but it is lacking in detail or not fully explained. ***[4 to 6 marks]***

Level 3: There is a thorough description of the advantages and disadvantages of reducing the price of Travel Bath and investing in new marketing material, with a detailed recommendation of what Bluebell Babies should do that has been fully explained. ***[7 to 9 marks]***

Here are some points your answer may include:

Reducing the price of the Travel Bath may make the product more desirable to customers since it will be closer to the price of its competitors. This may increase the sales and market share of the product. However, Bluebell Babies would earn less money per product sold. Also, reducing the price to £30 would still mean that the product is more expensive than all the other products on the market. So customers concerned about price may still not be likely to buy it.

It would also still be more expensive than BabyBath Deluxe, which customers considered to be the best quality portable baby bath. Therefore, lowering the price to £30 is unlikely to result in customers choosing Travel Bath over BabyBath Deluxe.

Only 10% of people surveyed were aware of Travel Bath. This is a lower percentage of people than for any of the other products. Therefore, investing in additional marketing may help to make customers more aware of the product. This could increase sales and market share of the product.

Additional marketing may also increase sales and market share of Travel Bath by persuading consumers that it is of higher quality than its competitors. This may also be less expensive for Bluebell Babies than reducing the price of the product since it is a one-off cost rather than a loss of profit on each item sold.

Make sure you finish your answer with a conclusion recommending what you think Bluebell Babies should do — it doesn't matter which you choose as long as you give reasons. E.g. 'Bluebell Babies should invest in additional marketing material for Travel Bath. Investing in additional marketing material is likely to increase the sales and market share of the product, but may not affect the profit per product sold as much as lowering the price of each product.'

Page 28 — Globalisation

1 A ***[1 mark]***

2.1 E.g. having a good design may help their products to stand out from the global competition ***[1 mark]***, which may mean that their sales will be increased ***[1 mark]***.

2.2 E.g. to offer products at lower prices than their competitors ***[1 mark]***. To offer higher quality products than their competitors ***[1 mark]***.

2.3 Any two from: e.g. globalisation means that Squishie has a larger market to sell to ***[1 mark]***, which may mean that they have increased sales / higher profits ***[1 mark]***. / Squishie (as a UK company) is able to source its raw materials from the same country in which it makes and packages its products ***[1 mark]***, which will reduce the cost of transporting the ingredients ***[1 mark]***. / Squishie is able to employ workers in Spain, where the minimum wage is lower than in the UK ***[1 mark]***, which will mean it has reduced costs ***[1 mark]***.

Page 29 — Exchange Rates

Warm-Up

imports, exports, cheaper

1 D *[1 mark]*

2.1 How to grade your answer:

Level 0: Nothing worthy of credit. *[No marks]*

Level 1: There is a basic description of the effect of the exchange rate changing on costs, but with little explanation of how this will affect the company. *[1 to 2 marks]*

Level 2: There is a detailed description of the effect of the exchange rate changing on costs, with a detailed explanation of how this will affect the company. *[3 to 4 marks]*

Here is an answer you could have written:

The amount of CNY which can be bought using INR for the same price has decreased / INR has become cheaper. So it will be cheaper for the Chinese phone manufacturing company to import raw materials from India. This means that they will be able to make their phones more cheaply so their profits may go up / so they may be able to sell their phones more cheaply.

2.2 How to grade your answer:

Level 0: Nothing worthy of credit. *[No marks]*

Level 1: There is a basic description of the effect of the exchange rate changing on prices, but with little explanation of how this will affect the company. *[1 to 2 marks]*

Level 2: There is a detailed description of the effect of the exchange rate changing on prices, with a detailed explanation of how this will affect the company. *[3 to 4 marks]*

Here is an answer you could have written:

The amount of CNY which can be bought using USD for the same price will have increased / USD has become more expensive, which means that the Chinese company's phones will be relatively cheaper to buy in the USA. This should result in greater sales of the phones and so greater profits for the Chinese company.

Page 30 — Risks in Business

1.1 Any three from: e.g. in order to make money / to have the freedom to be her own boss / to leave a job she doesn't enjoy / to follow an interest / to have a challenge / to benefit other people. *[3 marks — 1 mark for each correct answer]*

1.2 E.g. if Tasty Teas doesn't make enough profit, then she might not be able to pay the money back *[1 mark]*, and her business may fail / she may lose money *[1 mark]*.

1.3 Hint: make sure you only consider risks that may be faced by established businesses. You get one mark for putting down a potential risk and one for explaining it.

E.g. the health of the economy may decline *[1 mark]*, which may reduce demand and therefore sales for Tasty Teas' ready meals *[1 mark]*. / Tasty Teas competitors may claim a larger market share *[1 mark]*, leading to a loss in sales for Tasty Teas *[1 mark]*.

1.4 Hint: here, you get one mark for stating one thing Louise could use her market research for, and one mark for explaining how this will reduce the risks to the business.

E.g. Louise's research into customer preferences will help her to create the correct marketing mix for her products *[1 mark]* and so will help to ensure that customers will want to buy her products *[1 mark]*. / Her research into her competitors will help her to keep up with any changes in her competitors' products or prices *[1 mark]* and so will help to keep her business competitive *[1 mark]*.

1.5 E.g. she could ensure that she is aware of any changes in the law / economic situation *[1 mark]*. She could put together detailed plans for different scenarios in the future *[1 mark]*.

Pages 31-32 — Supply Chains

Warm-Up

customers, raw materials, finished product, manufacturers

1 B *[1 mark]*

2 Any two from: e.g. working closely with suppliers ensures key processes are running efficiently / working closely with suppliers ensures key processes are running cost effectively / it means the company will find the best price/ value / it will reduce waste / it will reduce unnecessary costs. *[2 marks — 1 mark for each correct answer]*

3 E.g. Jemma will find / buy things that the firm needs from suppliers outside the firm *[1 mark]*. For example, raw materials such as glass *[1 mark]*.

4 E.g. the prices offered by the suppliers *[1 mark]*, the quality of the products offered by the suppliers *[1 mark]*, the reliability of the suppliers *[1 mark]*.

5.1 E.g. Shake it Up would need to arrange to collect the milk from the farm each morning *[1 mark]*. Shake it Up would need to arrange how the milkshakes were delivered from the factory to the cafés around the UK *[1 mark]*.

5.2 How to grade your answer:

Level 0: Nothing worthy of credit. *[No marks]*

Level 1: Some attempt to recommend what Shake it Up should do has been given, but with little explanation for why this should be done. *[1 to 3 marks]*

Level 2: Some of the advantages and disadvantages of each option have been given, along with a recommendation of what Shake it Up should do. There is some reasoning to the recommendation, but it is lacking in detail or not fully explained. *[4 to 6 marks]*

Level 3: There is a thorough description of the advantages and disadvantages of each option, with a detailed recommendation of what Shake it Up should do that has been fully explained. *[7 to 9 marks]*

Here are some points your answer may include:

Using the local farm

Buying cream from the farm means that Shake it Up can change their order up to 6pm the day before they collect it. Shake it Up are unsure what the demand for ice-cream will be, so being able to change their order at short notice and collect the cream every day should mean they are more likely to order the correct amount. This will improve efficiency and cut down on waste.

The farm is reliable, since it ensures that milk is ready for collection the morning after an order has been placed, so they are likely to be reliable in supplying cream as well.

Shake it Up know that the quality of produce from the farm is good, so buying from the farm should help to ensure the quality of the ice-cream is the same standard as the milkshakes.

The farm offers Shake it Up a discount on orders over £500. If they are ordering cream as well as milk from the farm, they are more likely to be buying this amount, so will benefit from reducing their costs by using the discount.

Shake it Up would have to collect the cream from the farm. They are already paying for someone to collect milk each day, but they may have to invest in a larger van if they are ordering more produce.

Using Ribblethwaites

The cream at Ribblethwaites is cheaper than from the farm, so Shake it Up's costs would be reduced.

Ribblethwaites will deliver the cream to Shake it Up, which will mean they don't have to spend pay for someone to collect the cream.

Shake it Up haven't used Ribblethwaites before, so don't know what the quality of the produce will be.

Ribblethwaites may also be unreliable.

Shake it Up would have to order cream a week in advance, which could lead to waste if they order too much or not being able to complete orders if they order too little.

Make sure you finish your answer with a conclusion recommending what you think Shake it Up should do — it doesn't matter which you choose as long as you give reasons. E.g. 'Shake it Up should buy cream from the farm. Even though it will be more expensive, this cost difference will be less if they are able to use their discount. The flexibility of being able to change the order up to 6pm the day before is a big advantage, as is the fact they know that the farm is reliable and supplies high quality produce.'

Page 33 — Methods of Production

1 A ***[1 mark]***

2 E.g. it can be very capital-intensive / it needs a lot of money to e.g. buy machinery ***[1 mark]***. It can mean that a firm needs lots of space to store products ***[1 mark]***.

3.1 Hint: there are two marks for stating an advantage and disadvantage of job production, and two marks for explaining their impact on the company.
E.g. the sofas made using job production can be made exactly to a customer's specification ***[1 mark]***, which could lead to better customer satisfaction ***[1 mark]***. However, making the sofas using job production is expensive, so could lead to high prices ***[1 mark]***, which could mean fewer customers buy sofas from the company, and their sales would be low ***[1 mark]***.

3.2 Flow production would allow them to make the identical sofas along an assembly line ***[1 mark]***. This would be cheaper/quicker than job production ***[1 mark]***, so Sofa-So-Good Ltd. would be able to earn more profit on each sofa of this type that is sold ***[1 mark]***.

Page 34 — Production Efficiency

Warm-Up

just-in-time — When a company aims to keep stock levels to a bare minimum.

lean production — When a business aims to use as few resources as possible and have as little waste as possible.

just-in-case — When a company makes sure it has buffer stocks of items at every stage in the process.

1.1 E.g. The Reading Shelf won't run out of books, even if there is a delay in the delivery of the books from their supplier ***[1 mark]***. The Reading Shelf is likely to have enough stock if the demand for books from the bookshops increases unexpectedly ***[1 mark]***.

1.2 How to grade your answer:
Level 0: Nothing worthy of credit. ***[No marks]***
Level 1: There is some attempt to state how changing to just-in-time (JIT) will affect the costs of The Reading Shelf, but there is little or no explanation of why these changes happen. ***[1 to 2 marks]***
Level 2: There is a basic analysis of how changing to JIT will affect the costs of The Reading Shelf, but the explanations are lacking in detail, or points have been missed. ***[3 to 4 marks]***
Level 3: There is a thorough analysis of how changing to JIT will affect the costs of The Reading Shelf, with detailed explanations of the causes of these effects. ***[5 to 6 marks]***

Here are some points your answer may include:

Switching to JIT means The Reading Shelf will no longer order books in bulk. It is therefore less likely to make orders over 2000 units and so will not benefit from the discount offered by the supplier on these large orders. Therefore, the costs of their supplies could increase.

Using JIT means The Reading Shelf will have more frequent deliveries. This means their costs will go up, as they'll have to pay a delivery charge each time.

The Reading Shelf will no longer need to rent such a large warehouse to store its books, so costs could go down.

Using JIT means The Reading Shelf will only order the stock they need, so won't have as much waste from discarding books that are no longer selling. This could mean their costs go down as they are only spending money on books they know they should sell.

Page 35 — Quality

1.1 Saif delivers the furniture promptly — within 48 hours of the customer making the order ***[1 mark]***. Saif will set up the customer's furniture for no extra cost ***[1 mark]***.

1.2 E.g. Saif should have given Alec staff training ***[1 mark]*** to make sure he was aware of how to do his job properly ***[1 mark]***.

1.3 How to grade your answer:
Level 0: Nothing worthy of credit. ***[No marks]***
Level 1: Some attempt to describe the impact Alec has had on quality, but with little analysis of how this may affect SB Vans. ***[1 to 2 marks]***
Level 2: There is a good explanation of the impact Alec has had on quality, with some analysis of how this may affect SB Vans. ***[3 to 4 marks]***
Level 3: There is a detailed explanation of the impact Alec has had on quality, and a clear analysis of how this may affect SB Vans. ***[5 to 6 marks]***

Here are some points your answer may include:

Since Alec started, the proportion of deliveries which have been delivered within Saif's target of 48 hours has fallen from 88% (24% + 64%) to 78% (24% + 54%). This may lead to customer complaints, as Saif guarantees delivery within 48 hours.

This could lead to the factories deciding not to use SB Vans as their courier service anymore, which would cause the business's sales to fall.

It could also give SB Vans a poor reputation and could lead to other factories not using the business, meaning it would lose potential sales.

Customers could also ask for compensation for the late deliveries, which may affect SB Vans' profits.

Page 36 — Quality Management

1 Outsourcing: e.g. it can be expensive to outsource to a firm with high quality standards / the outsourced firm may not deliver the same standard of quality as the company expects ***[1 mark]***.
Franchising: e.g. it takes a lot of time to train new staff / it can be expensive to carry out regular inspections on franchises ***[1 mark]***.

2.1 E.g. having workers on the production line check there aren't any problems with their stage before passing the car on would make sure each step in the process is delivered at a consistently high standard ***[1 mark]***. Testing a sample of the cars each day should help to identify any defects ***[1 mark]***.

2.2 How to grade your answer:
Level 0: Nothing worthy of credit. ***[No marks]***
Level 1: There is some attempt to state the effects of using TQM at Toyota, but there is little or no explanation of why these effects happen. ***[1 to 2 marks]***
Level 2: There is a basic analysis of how using TQM will affect Toyota, but the explanations are lacking in detail, or points have been missed. ***[3 to 4 marks]***
Level 3: There is a thorough analysis of how TQM will affect Toyota, with detailed explanations of the causes of these effects. ***[5 to 6 marks]***
Here are some points your answer may include:
Total quality management means that everyone at Toyota is responsible for making sure their work is delivered to a high standard.
This should mean things are done right first time, which will cut down on waste and cut down on costs.
It should also mean there are fewer customer complaints resulting from poor quality cars, so customer satisfaction will be higher. High customer satisfaction will mean that Toyota has a good reputation which should help to increase sales.
Workers need lots of training to make sure they recognise when something isn't up to standard, and how to fix it if it isn't.
This can increase costs and the amount of time it takes to train staff.
It could also cause staff to be demotivated if they feel they have to do a lot of extra work.
TQM has caused Toyota to win awards for its quality.
This should encourage customers to buy cars from Toyota, so their sales should be increased.

Pages 37-38 — Customer Service

Warm-Up
1. Finding customers. 2. Approaching customers. 3. Assessing customer needs. 4. Presenting the product to a customer.
5. Getting the customer to buy the item. 6. Following up with the customer after the sale.

1 A ***[1 mark]***

2.1 E.g. a business may be able to charge more for its products if it has good customer service ***[1 mark]*** since customers are sometimes prepared to pay a little more for a product if they feel they will receive better customer support ***[1 mark]***.

2.2 E.g. if customers are satisfied with the level of service they receive from a business, they may be more likely to buy products again from the business in the future / recommend it to friends ***[1 mark]***. This will lead to an increase in revenue ***[1 mark]***. If this increase outweighs any spending on improving customer service, then profits will rise ***[1 mark]***.

3.1 E.g. Durrell's provides good after sales service ***[1 mark]*** as the customer does not have to pay to return goods ***[1 mark]***.

3.2 Hint: there are three marks here — one for identifying a problem, one for explaining why it's a problem and one for explaining what could be done to fix the problem.
E.g. Durrell's currently provides a poor delivery service ***[1 mark]*** as it only dispatches products within four days of the given date 75% of the time ***[1 mark]***. The firm should improve this service so that it can keep to its dispatch dates more often ***[1 mark]***. / Durrell's currently provides poor customer support ***[1 mark]*** since it only answers 70% of customer calls ***[1 mark]***. The firm should improve this service so that it manages to answer more customer calls ***[1 mark]***.

3.3 Any two from: e.g. providing a frequently asked questions section / giving contact details / having an online form through which customers can make enquiries / having a 'live chat' feature that customers can use to talk to a customer service advisor ***[2 marks — 1 mark for each correct answer]***.

3.4 How to grade your answer:
Level 0: Nothing worthy of credit. ***[No marks]***
Level 1: Some impacts on Durrell's reputation have been identified, but with little explanation of why these could happen. ***[1 to 3 marks]***
Level 2: There is a basic explanation of some of the impacts that having a website and social media accounts may have on Durrell's reputation. There is some attempt to conclude whether there will be a mostly positive or negative impact, but with little or no explanation to justify the conclusion. ***[4 to 6 marks]***
Level 3: There is a detailed explanation of the impacts that having a website and social media accounts may have on Durrell's reputation. There is a conclusion as to whether there will be a mostly positive or negative impact, but the justification is lacking in detail. ***[7 to 9 marks]***
Level 4: There is a detailed and thorough analysis of how the website and social media accounts could affect Durrell's reputation. A conclusion has been made as to whether there will be a mostly positive or negative impact, which has been fully justified using evidence. ***[10 to 12 marks]***
Here are some points your answer may include:
Ways customer service will improve
Having a website means customers can buy products all day, so ordering is easier.
Having a website and social media accounts may mean that it will be quick and easy for customers to make enquiries. If Durrell's is quick at responding to these enquiries, it may help to improve customer support and therefore customer satisfaction.
If having a website and social media accounts improves customer satisfaction, customers are more likely to recommend Durrell's to others, and their reputation is likely to improve.

Problems Durrell's could have with providing customer service

Currently, Durrell's only dispatches 75% of products within four days of their dispatch date. This is a poor record.

Having a website is predicted to increase orders by 30%. If Durrell's fail to improve their dispatch system, the increase in orders is likely to mean they dispatch even fewer items on time.

Durrell's response rate to customer calls is at 70% which is not that high, and an increase in enquiries of 40% may mean that customer support will worsen.

These factors are likely to lead to customers being dissatisfied. These dissatisfied customers could tell other people not to buy from Durrell's, which would lead to them getting a poor reputation.

Customers could also complain on social media, which could give Durrell's a poor reputation if lots of other people see these complaints.

Make sure you finish your answer with a conclusion about what the overall effect on Durrell's reputation is likely to be — it doesn't matter whether you think it will be mostly positive or mostly negative as long as you give reasons. E.g. 'The overall effect on Durrell's reputation is likely to be negative. Their ability to deliver orders on time and answer customer enquiries is likely to get even worse with the increase in orders and enquiries, and this will lead to lots of complaints and high levels of customer dissatisfaction.'

Pages 39-41 — Internal Organisational Structures

Warm-Up

True, True, True, False

1 C ***[1 mark]***

2 E.g. decentralisation may result in inconsistencies developing between different departments within the company / the decision-makers not doing what's best for the overall needs of the company ***[1 mark]***. This is because in a decentralised structure the authority to make decisions is shared out ***[1 mark]***.

3 E.g. a wide span of control means that each manager is responsible for a lot of workers ***[1 mark]***. This can make it difficult for managers to monitor each worker effectively / can make verbal communication difficult if managers need to talk to each of their workers individually ***[1 mark]***.

4.1 E.g. Claire Wilkinson is likely to be responsible for the overall strategy of Houghton & Son ***[1 mark]***, whereas Liam McNulty is likely to be responsible for a specific project / small team of operatives ***[1 mark]***.

4.2 E.g. long chains of command mean that communication up and down the hierarchy can be difficult/slow / verbal communication can be difficult ***[1 mark]***. This is because there are more people that need to pass on the message in the chain / more managers that need to be involved in a conversation ***[1 mark]***.

4.3 E.g. the chains of command became longer because the business would have employed more people as it grew ***[1 mark]***, so more managers would have been needed to help to organise and control staff ***[1 mark]***.

4.4 Delayering means removing layers of management, usually from the middle layers of a hierarchy ***[1 mark]***. So the regional, district and branch sales managers will probably be most affected ***[1 mark]*** as they are at highest risk of losing their positions ***[1 mark]***.

5 How to grade your answer:

Level 0: Nothing worthy of credit. ***[No marks]***

Level 1: The student has stated some traits of both organisational structures, but with little explanation of how changing to the new organisational structure will affect CraftyCakes. ***[1 to 3 marks]***

Level 2: The student has given a basic explanation of how changing to the new organisational structure will affect CraftyCakes. There is some attempt to conclude which organisational structure will be most beneficial to CraftyCakes, but with little or no explanation to justify the conclusion. ***[4 to 6 marks]***

Level 3: There is a detailed description of the advantages and disadvantages of both organisational structures, with a well reasoned and fully explained recommendation of which organisational structure would be most beneficial to CraftyCakes. ***[7 to 9 marks]***

Level 4: There is a detailed and thorough analysis of the two organisational structures and how they would affect CraftyCakes. A conclusion has been made as to which organisational structure would be most beneficial, which has been fully justified using evidence. ***[10 to 12 marks]***

Here are some points your answer may include:

The new organisational structure (Figure 3) of CraftyCakes is organised into different sectors of the business.

This is an appropriate structure for the business as the running of the coffee shop side of the business is likely to be very different to the side which makes products for retailers.

An advantage of using this structure is that the managers will have lots of knowledge about their sector and will be able to make better decisions relating to that sector.

A disadvantage is that some resources will be duplicated between the different sectors and overall the company will have to employ more people. For example, it means employing twice as many Marketing, Finance and Production Directors than in the current organisational structure. This will increase the firm's costs. However, employing more people may also mean that the business will be able to expand more in the future and therefore lead to an increase in sales.

In a decentralised structure, authority is delegated more. The new organisational structure is more decentralised than the current one. This may mean that changes can be made more quickly, as the directors for the different parts of the business may not need to communicate their decisions with directors above them for approval.

However, having more people making important decisions can be a disadvantage, as it means that the decision-makers might not be able to see the overall needs of the business. It may also mean that inconsistencies develop between the two different sides of the business.

A chain of command is the chain that connects directors to operatives.

The new structure is taller than the current structure and has a longer chain of command between the Marketing Assistants and the Executive Director — there are six people in the chain compared to four.

Longer chains of command can be a disadvantage as they mean that communication up and down the hierarchy can be difficult and slow. They can also mean that verbal communication becomes difficult if lots of managers need to be involved in a conversation. When a discussion is needed, meetings may need to be set up in advance.
The span of control is the number of workers who report to one manager in a hierarchy.
Moving to the new structure would mean that the Retail Marketing Manager's span of control would become wider. Having a wider span of control could be a disadvantage because it means that the retail marketing manager would have more people to manage, which can be difficult to do effectively. A wider span of control may also make verbal communication more difficult if the manager needs to speak to each worker individually.

Make sure you finish your answer with a conclusion about which organisational structure would be most beneficial for CraftyCakes — it doesn't matter which you choose as long as you give reasons.
E.g. 'continuing with the current organisational structure would be more beneficial for the business. The structure is more centralised, meaning that inconsistencies are less likely to occur between the retail and the coffee shop sides of the business (e.g. the branding). The new structure would be more costly for the firm as it would mean employing more people and the chains of command would be longer, meaning that communication may become slower and more difficult.'

Page 42 — Contracts of Employment

1 In a part-time contract of employment the employee typically works between 10 and 30 hours each week ***[1 mark]***, whereas in a zero hours contract of employment the employee doesn't have any set number of hours that they work ***[1 mark]***.

2.1 E.g. employing four nursery supervisors part-time rather than three full-time would have allowed staff to be more flexible with their hours ***[1 mark]***. This means that Simon may well have had staff available to cover the hours while Carla was at her appointments ***[1 mark]***.

2.2 E.g.
Simon: The person recruited to job share might have different strengths to Carla to bring to the business. / The other person recruited might be able to work extra hours if Carla is absent. ***[1 mark]***.
Carla: Carla has requested to reduce her hours and the job share would allow her to work part-time hours ***[1 mark]***.

Pages 43-44 — Recruitment

1 B ***[1 mark]***

2 Any two from: e.g. the formal title of the job / the main purpose of the job / the main duties of the job / any occasional duties of the job / who the job holder reports to / whether the job holder will be responsible for any other staff ***[2 marks — 1 mark for each correct answer]***

3.1 Any two from: e.g. a CV / an application form / details of people who will give them references. ***[2 marks — 1 mark for each correct answer]***

3.2 E.g. a person specification would have given information about the qualities/experience Jasmine wants the new nail technician to have ***[1 mark]***. By not providing it Jasmine may waste time considering candidates who do not meet her requirements ***[1 mark]***.

3.3 Hint — in your answer make sure you show that you understand the purpose of interviews and tests and explain how they might help Jasmine to find a suitable person to fill her vacancy.
E.g. during an interview Jasmine can ask the candidates questions about their previous experience and assess whether their personality would be suitable for her salons ***[1 mark]***. Jasmine could use personality tests to assess the candidates' personal qualities / skills tests to assess the candidates' nail technician abilities ***[1 mark]***. By asking all of the candidates the same questions and giving them the same tests she can compare the responses ***[1 mark]***, which will help her to choose the most suitable person for the job ***[1 mark]***.

4.1 Any two from: e.g. appropriate qualifications in scientific disciplines / previous relevant experience in laboratories / the skills to do the job / the attitude needed for the job ***[2 marks — 1 mark for each correct answer.]***

4.2 Any two from: e.g. the adverts will be seen by more people ***[1 mark]*** so it's more likely that Chem and Co will find the qualified senior chemists needed for the roles ***[1 mark]***. / Recruiting people from outside of the business will mean that people with new ideas are brought in ***[1 mark]***, which could improve the quality of the drugs developed ***[1 mark]***. / Recruiting people from outside of the business will mean that there are no internal vacancies left to fill ***[1 mark]***, which would cost Chem and Co more time and money ***[1 mark]***.

5 How to grade your answer:
Level 0: Nothing worthy of credit. ***[No marks]***
Level 1: Some attempt to describe the benefits to the Horse and Foal of spending more time and money on recruitment, but with little explanation of how these benefits would come about. ***[1 to 2 marks]***
Level 2: There is a clear description of the benefits to the Horse and Foal of spending more time and money on recruitment, with some explanation of how these benefits would come about. ***[3 to 4 marks]***
Level 3: There is a detailed description of the benefits to the Horse and Foal of spending more time and money on recruitment, and a thorough explanation of how these benefits would come about. ***[5 to 6 marks]***

Here are some points your answer may include:
If the owners spent more time and money on recruitment they could do a job analysis for each vacancy in the pub. This would allow them to produce detailed job descriptions and person specifications for each role.
They could advertise the roles and include details of the job description and person specification in the adverts. This would help to make sure that only people who thought they were suited to the role would apply.
Recruiting the right people could make the pub more productive. This is because it's likely that less time and money will need to be spent training the new staff if they already have the skills needed.
Recruiting the right people could also mean that the new staff provide better customer service. A higher level of customer service could help the pub to increase the number of customers it has, meaning it could make more money.
Recruiting the right people will also help to make sure that the pub provides its customers with high quality products, such as good food. This could improve customer satisfaction and the reputation of the pub, meaning they get more customers and increased revenue.

Recruiting the right people could also help the pub to retain its staff. This would mean they didn't have the inconvenience and cost of having to regularly recruit and train new staff.

Page 45 — Staff Training

Warm-Up

on-the-job training — This training is done in the workplace once the person has started the job.

off-the-job training — This training often happens away from a person's workplace.

induction training — This training introduces new workers to the company before they start the job.

1 Hint — there are lots of possible answers here. For each benefit you mention, make sure you explain why it is beneficial to the business.
Any two from: e.g. trained staff should be better at their jobs ***[1 mark]***, which means they should be able to produce high quality goods / provide good customer service / be more efficient / be more productive ***[1 mark]***. / Training can help staff stay up to date with changes in the business, such as how to use new technology ***[1 mark]***, meaning staff can be better at their jobs ***[1 mark]***. / Training can help staff to feel like they're progressing in the firm ***[1 mark]***, which might make them stay with the firm for longer and reduce the firm's recruitment costs ***[1 mark]***.

2.1 E.g. new programming techniques are likely to be very technical/difficult to learn ***[1 mark]***, so it might be better if they are taught by people who are better qualified to teach them rather than by other employees ***[1 mark]***.

2.2 E.g. training at the university is likely to be more expensive than on-the-job training ***[1 mark]***, meaning that there is less money available to spend on other areas of the business ***[1 mark]***.

Page 46 — Financial Motivation

1 A salary is a fixed amount of payment, which doesn't change even if the number of hours worked does change ***[1 mark]***. Wages are paid based on the amount of work done, such as the number of hours worked ***[1 mark]***.

2 The staff may feel more motivated to work for the firm / to help the firm become more profitable ***[1 mark]***, since they will be given extra money (e.g. a share of the company's profits) on top of their basic pay ***[1 mark]***.

3.1 Money from salary = £15 000 ÷ 12 = £1250
Money from commission = (19 000 ÷ 100) × 5 = £950
Total amount paid = £1250 + £950 = **£2200** ***[3 marks for correct answer, otherwise 1 mark for calculating the money from his salary in March and 1 mark for calculating the money from commission]***

3.2 How to grade your answer:
Level 0: Nothing worthy of credit. ***[No marks]***
Level 1: Some attempt to recommend what Packman's Glazing should do has been given, but with little explanation for why this should be done. ***[1 to 3 marks]***
Level 2: Some of the advantages and disadvantages of the two pay schemes have been described, along with a recommendation of which one Packman's Glazing should use. There is some reasoning to the recommendation, but it is lacking in detail or not fully explained. ***[4 to 6 marks]***
Level 3: There is a thorough description of the advantages and disadvantages of the two pay schemes, with a detailed and fully explained recommendation of which one Packman's Glazing should use. ***[7 to 9 marks]***

Here are some points your answer may include:
Paying sales staff commission will make them more motivated to sell, since the more they sell the more they earn. This will lead to higher productivity in the business. Having motivated staff can also increase staff retention as workers are less likely to want to leave the business. This can reduce recruitment and training costs for the business.
However, two of the sales staff have chosen to leave the business, partly because they would prefer to be paid a higher salary but with no commission.
Workers may prefer this pay scheme as it means they get a higher guaranteed income and they don't have the stress of having to sell lots of products in order to increase their income.
But this scheme may mean that productivity falls as the workers are less motivated to perform well. So moving to this pay scheme could mean that Packman's Glazing's profits would fall, as they would be paying their workers more but may experience falling sales.
As the rival firm is new, it may be too early to tell whether their pay scheme is effective at keeping workers motivated enough to stay with the firm long-term and to sell enough products.

Make sure you finish your answer with a conclusion recommending what you think Packman's Glazing should do — it doesn't matter what you recommend as long as you give reasons. E.g. 'Packman's Glazing should continue with their current pay scheme. Even though this means that they risk losing staff, their workers are likely to be more motivated to perform well, which could lead to more sales and higher profits for the business.'

Page 47 — Non-Financial Motivation

1 By learning new skills, staff can start to take on new tasks / have greater responsibility ***[1 mark]***. This may mean that they have greater self-esteem / they could get a promotion in the future ***[1 mark]***.

2.1 Hint — there are lots of examples of fringe benefits that you could give. Make sure that whatever example you give is realistic for staff in a shoe shop.
E.g. Meera could offer her employees a discount off shoes from the shop ***[1 mark]***, which would help them to feel motivated as they would save money ***[1 mark]***.

2.2 How to grade your answer:
Level 0: Nothing worthy of credit. ***[No marks]***
Level 1: Some attempt to describe how Meera's management style and actions are likely to affect her employees, but little analysis of how their level of motivation could be affected. ***[1 to 2 marks]***
Level 2: There is a clear description of how Meera's management style and actions are likely to affect her employees, including some analysis of how their level of motivation could be affected. ***[3 to 4 marks]***
Level 3: There is a detailed description of how Meera's management style and actions are likely to affect her employees, including a clear analysis of how their level of motivation could be affected. ***[5 to 6 marks]***

Here are some points your answer may include:
Meera has an authoritarian management style. This may make employees feel demotivated as it suggests their views aren't valued.
Meera's strict training programme may not make new workers feel very motivated if they feel under pressure when she is monitoring them closely. They may also not feel very motivated if the strict training programme means Meera is slow to give them any responsibility.
However, making sure that staff are properly trained may make staff more motivated in the long run as it may boost their self-esteem if they know they are good at their job.
The monthly meetings may help the staff to feel more motivated as they can have their views heard and their questions answered.
The employee of the month badge may also make the staff feel more motivated as it helps them to feel that their hard work is recognised and valued.

You could have put here that the meetings were too infrequent to motivate staff, or that the badge may have made some employees feel patronised and demotivated. You would still get marks in the exam as long as you'd backed up your ideas with good reasons.

Page 48 — The Marketing Mix

1 product ***[1 mark]***, place ***[1 mark]***

2.1 E.g. Williamson's sells essential kitchenware items ***[1 mark]***, which are likely to meet their customers' needs / which customers are likely to want to buy ***[1 mark]***.

2.2 How to grade your answer:

Level 0: Nothing worthy of credit. ***[No marks]***

Level 1: Some impacts the opening of DiscountDishes may have on Williamson's marketing mix have been described, but with little explanation of how DiscountDishes may cause these impacts. ***[1 to 3 marks]***

Level 2: There is a basic explanation of some of the impacts that the opening of DiscountDishes may have on the prices and promotion of Williamson's. There is some attempt to conclude whether price or promotion will be most affected, but with little or no explanation to justify the conclusion. ***[4 to 6 marks]***

Level 3: There is a detailed description of the impacts that the opening of DiscountDishes may have on the prices and promotion of Williamson's. There is a conclusion as to which aspect will be most affected, but the justification is lacking in detail. ***[7 to 9 marks]***

Level 4: There is a detailed and thorough analysis of the impact that the opening of DiscountDishes may have on the prices and promotion of Williamson's. A conclusion has been made as to which will be most affected, which has been fully justified using evidence. ***[10 to 12 marks]***

Here are some points your answer may include:
The price a company chooses must be set at a level that customers see as good value.
DiscountDishes sells similar items at a cheaper price than Williamson's. Therefore it may take some customers from Williamson's.
Currently, Williamson's has a cost-plus pricing strategy, where all products are sold at a 15% profit margin.
Williamson's may have to lower its prices (e.g. use a competitive pricing strategy) and charge similar prices to DiscountDishes in order to avoid losing customers.
However, Williamson's products are a higher quality, so customers may be happy to pay the higher price.
Promotion is needed so customers are aware a company exists.
Williamson's doesn't currently have very effective promotion, as most of the customers have heard about the shop from friends, rather than from promotional material.
DiscountDishes have put up posters in the shopping centre, so any customers in the shopping centre who are looking to find kitchenware may be more likely to go to DiscountDishes than Williamson's, as they will know they're there.
DiscountDishes are also offering a free gift to customers who spend more than £15, which may persuade customers to go there, rather than Williamson's.
Therefore Williamson's may decide to increase the amount it spends on promoting its store, in order to make more customers aware that it is there.
Williamson's could also emphasise the high quality of its products in its promotional material in order to attract more customers and differentiate itself from DiscountDishes.

Make sure you finish your answer with a conclusion about whether price or promotion in Williamson's marketing mix will be most affected — it doesn't matter which you choose as long as you give reasons. E.g. 'Williamson's promotional strategy is likely to be more affected than its pricing strategy. This is because by changing its promotional activities it may be able to stay competitive with DiscountDishes without sacrificing the profit it makes on each product.'

Page 49 — Market Research

1 A ***[1 mark]***

2.1 Segmentation is when people within a market are divided into different groups ***[1 mark]***, for example by age/income/location/gender ***[1 mark]***.

2.2 E.g. so that the business can create a targeted marketing strategy ***[1 mark]*** which will mean that the business doesn't waste money by creating ineffective promotional material / by creating a product the target market won't buy ***[1 mark]***.

3.1 E.g. their products ***[1 mark]*** and prices ***[1 mark]***.

3.2 Any two from: e.g. by knowing their customers' needs, Davis and Sons can make sure that they sell suits in colours that their customers will buy ***[1 mark]***. / They can avoid spending money on suits in colours their customers won't buy ***[1 mark]***. / They can be competitive against other suit sellers ***[1 mark]***. / Davis and Sons can choose the correct marketing mix for their suits ***[1 mark]***.

Page 50 — Types of Market Research

1 B ***[1 mark]***

2.1 E.g. the focus groups should use people from the correct market segment / people who are over the age of 70 ***[1 mark]***, so that the information gathered is useful for the business ***[1 mark]***.

2.2 E.g. they can provide more in-depth information ***[1 mark]***. They can be cheaper than interviewing individuals separately ***[1 mark]***.

3.1 E.g. a small business may prefer secondary research because it is cheaper ***[1 mark]*** and the data is also easily found / instantly available ***[1 mark]***.

3.2 Any two from: e.g. it isn't always relevant to the business ***[1 mark]***. / It's not specifically about the products of the business ***[1 mark]***. / It may be out of date ***[1 mark]***.

3.3 How to grade your answer:
Level 0: Nothing worthy of credit. ***[No marks]***
Level 1: Some attempt to recommend what form of research Jackie should use, but with little explanation for why this should be done. ***[1 to 3 marks]***
Level 2: Some of the advantages and disadvantages of the different forms of research have been given, along with a recommendation of what Jackie should use. There is some reasoning to the recommendation, but it is lacking in detail or not fully explained. ***[4 to 6 marks]***
Level 3: There is a thorough description of the advantages and disadvantages of the different forms of market research, with a detailed recommendation of what Jackie should do that has been fully explained. ***[7 to 9 marks]***

Here are some points your answer may include:
Interviews:
If Jackie carries out interviews she may be able to get information from the business owners that she is most interested in selling to. They may be able to give her the detailed information that she wants on the sales of different sandwiches and customer preferences more easily than if she used online questionnaires.
However, it takes a lot of time to conduct face-to-face interviews.
Online questionnaires:
An online questionnaire would allow Jackie to reach many more people than interviews. However, since her business is new, she may not get many visitors to her website, and therefore may not get as many responses as she would like.
She is also only interested in selling her sandwiches to specific cafes in her local area, and with an online questionnaire she wouldn't be able to target these specific cafes.
However, she may be able to get more feedback on customer preferences directly from customers.
Make sure you finish your answer with a conclusion recommending what you think Jackie should do — it doesn't matter which you choose as long as you give reasons. E.g. 'Jackie should use interviews. Although they take more time, she is more likely to get the information that she is most interested in.'

Pages 51-52 — Using Market Research

Warm-Up
quantitative, qualitative, quantitative, quantitative

1 How to grade your answer:
Level 0: Nothing worthy of credit. ***[No marks]***
Level 1: Some attempt to describe how the market research may affect Tom's Teas but with little analysis of why it may have these effects. ***[1 to 2 marks]***
Level 2: A number of effects of the market research on Tom's Teas have been described, with some analysis of why it is likely to have these effects. ***[3 to 4 marks]***
Level 3: There is a detailed description of the likely effects that the market research will have on Tom's Teas, and a clear analysis of why it may have these effects. ***[5 to 6 marks]***

Here are some points your answer may include:
Tom may be interested in selling the Jasmine deluxe tea in his shop, since this was the most popular tea on his questionnaire.
He will probably choose not to sell his liquorice and mint tea since it had a very low popularity of only 4% and many respondents had a strong dislike of the tea and thought that it tasted bitter.
He is also unlikely to sell the camomile and nettle tea since it also had a low popularity of only 10%. Despite the fact that there were few complaints about this tea, it is unlikely that he would sell enough of the tea for it to be worth his while blending and selling it.
A majority of respondents to the questionnaire stated that they would be unlikely to order one of the three teas instead of another drink in his shop. Therefore it would only be worth blending and selling the Jasmine deluxe tea since it was the most popular and he is unlikely to sell many of these new teas anyway.

2.1 How to grade your answer:
Level 0: Nothing worthy of credit. ***[No marks]***
Level 1: Some attempt to describe the effect of changing the flyers on Georgina's sales but with little analysis of why the changes are likely to have this effect. ***[1 to 2 marks]***
Level 2: A number of effects of changing the flyers on Georgina's sales have been described, with some analysis of why the changes are likely to have these effects. ***[3 to 4 marks]***
Level 3: There is a detailed description of the effects that changing the flyers are likely to have on Georgina's sales, and a clear analysis of why the changes are likely to have these effects. ***[5 to 6 marks]***

Here are some points your answer may include:
Georgina's original flyers prioritised showing the location and prices of the restaurant.
However, the market research data shows that for all but a few customers, location is not the most important aspect of the restaurant.
In addition, only 25% of respondents said price was the most important aspect of the restaurant in 2012, and this had dropped to 16% by 2017.
Georgina's new flyers prioritise the atmosphere of the restaurant, by showing an image of the inside and advertising music events that she is holding.
In 2017, atmosphere was the most popular response for the most important aspect of the restaurant.
The percentage of respondents who said atmosphere was most important increased between 2012 and 2017.
So by promoting the atmosphere of her restaurant, Georgina is likely to appeal to more customers than she did before. So more customers are likely to visit her restaurant and her sales are likely to increase.

2.2 How to grade your answer:
Level 0: Nothing worthy of credit. ***[No marks]***
Level 1: Some attempt to recommend which improvement Georgina should make, but with little explanation for why this should be done. ***[1 to 3 marks]***
Level 2: Some of the advantages and disadvantages of the different options for improving her restaurant have been given, along with a recommendation of what Georgina should do. There is some reasoning to the recommendation, but it is lacking in detail or not fully explained. ***[4 to 6 marks]***

Level 3: There is a thorough description of the advantages and disadvantages of the different options for improving her restaurant, with a detailed recommendation of what Georgina should do that has been fully explained. ***[7 to 9 marks]***

Here are some points your answer may include:

Improving the decorations and furniture:

Georgina's customers are likely to be more satisfied if she improves the decorations and furniture, since 42% of them said that the atmosphere of a restaurant was the most important aspect to them. This is a greater percentage than those who said that the choice of food was the most important aspect to them, so it may be more beneficial than increasing the size of the menu.

There has been an increase of 4.5% of customers saying that atmosphere is the most important aspect to them since 2012, suggesting that atmosphere is becoming more important to customers. Therefore improving the decorations and furniture may also attract new customers.

However, the atmosphere of the restaurant may depend on more than just the decorations and furniture. So changing these aspects of the restaurant's appearance may not necessarily affect the restaurant's atmosphere.

It may also be costly for Georgina to change the appearance of her restaurant.

Increasing the number of choices on the menu:

A high percentage of customers (39%) said that the choice of food was the most important aspect to them, so increasing the choice of food available may lead to more satisfied customers.

There has been an increase of 6.5% of customers saying that choice of food is the most important aspect for them, since 2012. This is a greater increase than for atmosphere, so the choice of food has become more important by a greater degree than atmosphere. Therefore it may be more beneficial for Georgina to increase the choice on the menu.

However, increasing the choice on the menu may affect the running of her restaurant, since her cooks will have to be able to make more dishes and she may have to buy in different ingredients.

It may also increase her costs, as she may need to purchase more types of ingredients.

Make sure you finish your answer with a conclusion recommending what you think Georgina should do — it doesn't matter which you choose as long as you give reasons. E.g. 'Georgina should improve the decorations and furniture. Although this may be costly, she is likely to have more satisfied customers and it won't affect the running of the restaurant.'

Page 53 — Product Life Cycles

1 A ***[1 mark]***

2.1 Research is carried out ***[1 mark]*** and the idea for the product is then developed to create a marketable product ***[1 mark]***.

2.2 How to grade your answer:

Level 0: Nothing worthy of credit. ***[No marks]***

Level 1: Some attempt to describe how Leafery Ltd. might change their marketing mix, but with little analysis of why this might be done. ***[1 to 2 marks]***

Level 2: The ways in which Leafery Ltd. might change the marketing mix have been described, with some analysis of why this might be done. ***[3 to 4 marks]***

Level 3: There is a detailed description of the ways in which Leafery Ltd. might change the marketing mix, and a clear analysis of why this might be done. ***[5 to 6 marks]***

Here are some points your answer may include:

When the product was launched, Leafery Ltd. prioritised promotion of the product.

This would have made customers aware of the product, and persuaded them to try the product, so would have increased demand.

As the product enters the maturity stage, it should have built up an established market, and demand should be at a peak.

So Leafery Ltd. are likely to spend less on promoting the product.

When the product was launched, Leafery Ltd. charged a low price for the product, which would have made customers more willing to try it.

By the time the weedkiller is entering the maturity stage, customers should be loyal to using it.

So Leafery Ltd. should be able to increase the price so they can make more of a profit, without losing much demand.

Page 54 — Extension Strategies

1 How to grade your answer:

Level 0: Nothing worthy of credit. ***[No marks]***

Level 1: There is a basic description of the effect of lowering the price on sales of the AddictaBox, but with little explanation of how this will affect RSI Gaming Ltd. ***[1 to 2 marks]***

Level 2: There is a detailed description of the effect of lowering the price on sales of the AddictaBox, with a detailed explanation of how this will affect RSI Gaming Ltd. ***[3 to 4 marks]***

Here is an answer you could have written:

The AddictaBox is in the decline phase of its life cycle, so sales are decreasing. Lowering the price may mean that more customers will be willing to buy the AddictaBox, which will extend its life and mean RSI Gaming Ltd.'s revenue from this product doesn't fall so quickly.

2 How to grade your answer:

Level 0: Nothing worthy of credit. ***[No marks]***

Level 1: Some attempt to explain the different extension strategies that Nestlé® have used but with little analysis of how effective each one is. ***[1 to 2 marks]***

Level 2: A number of the extension strategies that Nestlé® have used have been explained, with some analysis of how effective each one is. ***[3 to 4 marks]***

Level 3: There is a detailed explanation of the different extension strategies that Nestlé® have used, and a clear analysis of how effective each one is. ***[5 to 6 marks]***

Here are some points your answer may include:

By launching the KitKat® Chunky and making the chocolate bars available in many different flavours, Nestlé® was able to increase the demand for the product.

This may also have attracted new customers or a new target market that are more interested in the different forms of chocolate bar.

Because of this extension strategy, KitKat® remained one of the most popular chocolate bars in the market.

However, it was not enough to ensure its continued success as in 2014 KitKat® sales and market share decreased.

In response, Nestlé® changed the packaging of KitKat®s, which is likely to have made them more eye-catching and so persuade more customers to buy them over other products.
They also added a feature to the packaging that included a link to an online video.
This may have meant customers were more interested in buying the chocolate in order to watch the video and this may have increased sales.
Market research firm YouGov found via its daily BrandIndex service that, after the launch of this campaign, the proportion of UK consumers 18+ who had bought a KitKat® in the last 30 days increased from 11% to 17%.
This shows that demand increased, and so the campaign had been successful at extending the life of the product.

Page 55 — Product Portfolios

1 E.g. a balanced portfolio contains a range of product types ***[1 mark]***. If one product fails in a balanced portfolio, the business should still be able to depend on their other products to earn money ***[1 mark]***.
2.1 B ***[1 mark]***, because it has a low market share ***[1 mark]*** and is in a high growth market ***[1 mark]***.
2.2 A ***[1 mark]***, because it has a high market share ***[1 mark]*** and is in a high growth market ***[1 mark]***.
2.3 It's unlikely that the business will earn much from the product ***[1 mark]***, because it has a low market share ***[1 mark]*** and is in a slow growing market ***[1 mark]***.
2.4 A "cash cow" is a product with a high market share ***[1 mark]*** and is in a slow growing market ***[1 mark]***.

Pages 56-57 — Product Development

Warm-Up
customer preferences, the cost of the product and competitors' designs.
1 C ***[1 mark]***
2.1 By understanding their target market, they can create cars that they know their target market wants ***[1 mark]***. Therefore they will be more likely to sell their cars to their target market ***[1 mark]***, and so are more likely to get a return on their investment / less likely to make a costly mistake ***[1 mark]***.
2.2 E.g. it is a completely new product ***[1 mark]***, so they risk running out of money ***[1 mark]*** if they spend too much time and money developing the car and don't get it to market quickly enough ***[1 mark]***.
2.3 Hint: you get one mark for stating a potential benefit for Awoocar, and one mark for explaining this benefit.
E.g. they may appeal to a new market segment ***[1 mark]***, since the new car will attract a different type of customer ***[1 mark]***. / They may improve their reputation ***[1 mark]***, since customers may begin to associate the brand with a higher quality market ***[1 mark]***. / They may earn more money from selling a luxury model ***[1 mark]***, since they will be able to sell it at a higher price ***[1 mark]***.
3.1 E.g. it has three "cash cows" ***[1 mark]***, so it would probably have enough money to develop a new product ***[1 mark]***.
3.2 E.g. it doesn't have any "stars", which means that if its "cash cows" enter their decline phase it may start to run out of money ***[1 mark]***, therefore it may be too risky to spend money on developing more products ***[1 mark]***. It already has three "question marks" ***[1 mark]***, therefore it might be better investing its money in promoting these products instead ***[1 mark]***.
4.1 E.g. it's important so that the company's overall brand image remains strong ***[1 mark]***, since this will mean that all of the company's products will be more easily recognised ***[1 mark]*** and will be more likely to be bought by customers ***[1 mark]***.
4.2 Hint: there are two marks for this question, so make sure you fully explain why sales may be increased.
E.g. having a different scent will give the conditioner a unique selling point ***[1 mark]*** which may make it more desirable than competitors' conditioners to customers ***[1 mark]***.
4.3 E.g. it is important that the conditioner is of acceptable quality ***[1 mark]***, so that the product develops a good brand image ***[1 mark]*** and customers want to buy it ***[1 mark]***.

Page 58 — Price

1 A ***[1 mark]***
2.1 How to grade your answer:
Level 0: Nothing worthy of credit. ***[No marks]***
Level 1: There is a basic description of why prices might be lowered, but with little explanation of what may cause the lower prices. ***[1 to 2 marks]***
Level 2: There is a detailed description of why prices might be lowered, with a detailed explanation of what may cause the lower prices. ***[3 to 4 marks]***
Here is an answer you could have written:
E.g. as Pottery Wheel starts to produce more pottery, it will order clay in larger quantities. As the size of the order of clay increases, it becomes cheaper per kg. So Pottery Wheel's costs per unit will go down and it will be able to lower its prices whilst still making a profit.
2.2 The Indigo Night collection is in the decline phase, so demand is falling ***[1 mark]***. Decreasing the price should increase demand for the collection again ***[1 mark]***.
2.3 E.g. the Crystal Gold collection is being marketed as a more luxurious collection / is being targeted at a different market segment / is of higher quality than the other collections ***[1 mark]***. So customers may be more willing to pay more for the collection ***[1 mark]***.

Pages 59-60 — Pricing Strategies

1 B ***[1 mark]***
2 Competitive pricing is when a firm charges similar prices to other firms ***[1 mark]***. A company may use competitive pricing if the market is very competitive ***[1 mark]*** and there is not much product differentiation ***[1 mark]***.
3.1 A price penetration strategy ***[1 mark]***, because the price being charged is very low compared to the average ***[1 mark]***.
3.2 E.g. Video Box Ltd. ***[1 mark]***, because it has a very low market share compared to the other major companies ***[1 mark]*** and charging a very low price for its service may help it to increase its market share ***[1 mark]***.
4.1 Mark-up = $4.40 \times 0.7 = 3.08$
Cost = $4.40 + 3.08 =$ **£7.48** ***[2 marks for correct answer, otherwise 1 mark for correctly calculating mark-up]***
4.2 E.g. a cost-plus pricing strategy is suitable when the product isn't in price competition with other producers ***[1 mark]***. This is the case for ElectricPages Ltd.'s e-books, as only they sell e-books that are compatible with the EezyReadr ***[1 mark]***. So they can choose a price to give them the profit they want while still having reasonable demand, and won't lose customers to other e-book sellers ***[1 mark]***.

4.3 How to grade your answer:

Level 0: Nothing worthy of credit. ***[No marks]***

Level 1: Some attempt to recommend what pricing strategy ElectricPages Ltd. should use, but with little explanation for why this should be done. ***[1 to 3 marks]***

Level 2: Some of the advantages and disadvantages of both strategies have been given, along with a recommendation for which one ElectricPages Ltd. should use. There is some reasoning to the recommendation, but it is lacking in detail or not fully explained. ***[4 to 6 marks]***

Level 3: There is a thorough description of the advantages and disadvantages of both strategies, with a detailed recommendation of which strategy ElectricPages Ltd. should use that has been fully explained. ***[7 to 9 marks]***

Here are some points your answer may include:

Loss leader:

With a loss leader strategy, the new e-reader would generate a loss per product sold. Therefore this strategy would be very costly for ElectricPages Ltd. The company is also new, so it may not have many other products to sell in order to cover its costs on selling the EezyReadr at a loss. So a loss leader strategy may be too risky.

However using a loss leader strategy may mean that the e-reader will be cheaper than other e-readers on the market, which will encourage people to buy it. This will help to establish a market share.

E-books are much cheaper to make than e-readers and the company keeps a large percentage of the sales of e-books as profit.

By using a loss leader strategy, the company will encourage customers to buy their e-books, since only e-books bought from ElectricPages Ltd.'s website are compatible with the device. Therefore, even though they will make a loss on the EezyReadr using this strategy, they could still earn profit through sales of e-books from their website.

Price skimming:

With a price skimming strategy, the EezyReadr would be sold at a high price. This would be beneficial for ElectricPages Ltd. since they would be able to cover the costs of the research and development of the EezyReadr and may make a profit.

A price skimming strategy may be suitable for the EezyReadr because it may have a high demand when it is first introduced due to its new technological features.

However, the company is new, and so it is unlikely to have many loyal customers who would be willing to pay a high price for the new product.

Although it has new features, it is not the first e-reader on the market, so it might not benefit very much from a price skimming strategy as there might not be enough demand for the EezyReadr.

A price skimming strategy may give the EezyReadr a good image, which would help to establish ElectricPages Ltd.'s brand image.

Make sure you finish your answer with a conclusion recommending what you think ElectricPages Ltd. should do — it doesn't matter which you choose as long as you give reasons. E.g. 'ElectricPages Ltd. should use a loss leader pricing strategy for their new EezyReadr. Although they will earn less profit per e-reader sold, they are likely to attract more customers and make more profit through sales of e-books.'

Pages 61-62 — Methods of Promotion

Warm-Up

Internet advert — It can include a link to a firm's website.

Billboard — It can stay in place for a long time.

Magazine advert — It can target a specialist market.

1 Any two from: e.g. to remind customers about the product / to increase sales / to change the image of the product / to persuade more customers to buy the product ***[2 marks — 1 mark for each correct answer]***.

2 The business gives money towards the event and in exchange the name of the business is displayed at the event ***[1 mark]***. This means that the business might get a higher profile / more customers will know about the business ***[1 mark]***.

3.1 Any three from: e.g. who their target market is / what their competitors are doing / the nature of the market / the type of product that they are selling / the finance they have available ***[3 marks — 1 mark for each correct answer]***.

3.2 The business will have little control over what the magazine publishes ***[1 mark]***. If the magazine publishes a negative picture of Mamo Ltd. it may gain a bad reputation ***[1 mark]***.

4.1 E.g. free samples of food ***[1 mark]*** and a competition to win a discount on a catering package ***[1 mark]***.

4.2 Hint: you get one mark for giving a disadvantage of sales promotion and one mark for explaining how it might affect Bethany's business.

E.g. it might make her company seem like less of a luxury brand ***[1 mark]***, which may make her company less attractive to potential customers ***[1 mark]***. / It may mean that customers will not be willing to pay the normal price for her services ***[1 mark]*** and so may mean that she will earn less for her services / will lose out on potential sales ***[1 mark]***.

4.3 How to grade your answer:

Level 0: Nothing worthy of credit. ***[No marks]***

Level 1: Some attempt to describe how Beth's Kitchen could use social media for promotion, but with little analysis of whether they would be effective for the company. ***[1 to 2 marks]***

Level 2: A number of ways that Beth's Kitchen could use social media for promotion have been described, with some analysis of whether they would be effective for the company. ***[3 to 4 marks]***

Level 3: There is a detailed description of the ways that Beth's Kitchen could use social media for promotion, and a clear analysis of whether they would be effective for the company. ***[5 to 6 marks]***

Here are some points your answer may include:

A social media account is quick and easy to set up.

It is also a very cheap way for Beth's Kitchen to promote itself. This is useful, since Beth's Kitchen is relatively new and may not have much money available for other forms of promotion.

A social media account would allow Bethany to share customers' pictures and reviews. She could also offer promotions and advertise new catering packages. This may help to improve the reputation of Beth's Kitchen and attract new customers.

She can add information to the social media page whenever she wants, so if there are new offers available, or Beth's Kitchen is unable to take further bookings, she would be able to inform customers quickly.

Bethany takes bookings for Beth's Kitchen mainly through the company's website. It would be easy for customers to go from the social media page to the company's website, making it easy for customers to book with the catering company.
However, if the company makes any mistakes, then it is easy for customers to provide negative comments that can be seen quickly by lots of people. This means that time has to be spent monitoring the site.
Since Bethany is the only member of office staff, she would be the only one monitoring the site, and she might not have enough time to do this.

Page 63 — Place

1 A *[1 mark]*

2.1 Wholesalers order products in bulk ***[1 mark]*** and Lisa doesn't make products in large enough quantities to sell to a wholesaler ***[1 mark]***.

2.2 Hint: you get one mark for giving a disadvantage of selling directly to customers and one mark for explaining this disadvantage.
E.g. it may be time-consuming ***[1 mark]***, because she will have to arrange all the sales with individual customers ***[1 mark]***. / It may be difficult/expensive ***[1 mark]***, because she will have to arrange the delivery of the goods to different customers ***[1 mark]***.

3 How to grade your answer:
Level 0: Nothing worthy of credit. ***[No marks]***
Level 1: Some attempt to recommend what Eric should do has been given, but with little explanation for why this should be done. ***[1 to 3 marks]***
Level 2: Some of the advantages and disadvantages of using both the retailers and the wholesaler have been given, along with a recommendation of what Eric should do. There is some reasoning to the recommendation, but it is lacking in detail or not fully explained. ***[4 to 6 marks]***
Level 3: There is a thorough description of the advantages and disadvantages of using both the retailers and the wholesaler, with a detailed recommendation of what Eric should do that has been fully explained. ***[7 to 9 marks]***
Here are some points your answer may include:
Each month, the wholesaler will buy more stock (1400 units) than both of the retailers combined (1000 units). Therefore Eric will be able to sell more of his stock through the wholesaler. However, Eric is also renting out a new warehouse, so he will be able to store any stock that he doesn't sell immediately.
The wholesaler sells to retailers across the country and the retailers only sell to customers in his local area, so if he sells to the wholesalers his products will be sold in more locations and are likely to reach more customers.
If he sells through the wholesaler then he will earn less per unit than if he sells directly to the retailers.
If he sells to the retailers he will earn $(400 \times 70) + (600 \times 80) = £76\ 000$. This is more than if he sold to the wholesaler ($1400 \times 50 = £70\ 000$).
The channel of distribution using the wholesalers is also longer than if he were to sell directly to the retailers, which may mean that the products are more expensive for customers since both the wholesaler and the separate retailers will have to earn a profit for each item sold.
Therefore there may be more demand for his products if he sells directly through the retailers, because they may be cheaper.
Eric may be able to provide the retailers with product knowledge in order to help them offer customer service to customers, such as helping to install the spare laptop parts. This could improve customer satisfaction with his products.
Eric will have less contact with the retailers that the wholesaler sells to, so they may not be able to provide as much product knowledge to these retailers. This may mean that the customer service offered by these retailers is of lower quality, which may lead to reduced customer satisfaction with his products.

Make sure you finish your answer with a conclusion recommending what you think Eric should do — it doesn't matter which you choose as long as you give reasons. E.g. 'Eric should use the retailers. Although his stock will be sold in fewer locations than with the wholesaler, overall he will earn more each month and the retailers are also more likely to provide customer service for the products.'

Pages 64-65 — E-commerce

Warm-Up
buying an app using a smartphone, using a tablet to order groceries and using an e-reader to buy an e-book.

1 C ***[1 mark]***

2.1 M-commerce is when goods and services are bought using a wireless device ***[1 mark]***. British Bikes Ltd. have created a mobile phone app which can be used by customers to buy products ***[1 mark]***.

2.2 British Bikes Ltd. is likely to have increased sales as a result of m-commerce ***[1 mark]***, since people will be able to access their products in many different locations and situations ***[1 mark]***.

2.3 E.g. British Bikes Ltd. need their technology to stay up-to-date ***[1 mark]***, or customers may choose to buy their products from a more up-to-date competitor ***[1 mark]***.

3.1 The revenue for the high street stores decreases from between 2011/12 and 2014/15 ***[1 mark]***, because more customers are buying products from the website than in store ***[1 mark]***.

3.2 How to grade your answer:
Level 0: Nothing worthy of credit. ***[No marks]***
Level 1: Some attempt to describe how the new website may have affected Topstitch but with little analysis of how profit may have been affected. ***[1 to 2 marks]***
Level 2: A number of ways in which the new website may have affected Topstitch have been described, with some analysis of how profit may have been affected. ***[3 to 4 marks]***
Level 3: There is a detailed description of the ways in which the new website may have affected Topstitch, and a clear analysis of how profit may have been affected. ***[5 to 6 marks]***
Here are some points your answer may include:
It costs money to create and maintain a website, so this cost may have reduced the profits of the company.
The new website has led to dramatically increased sales for Topstitch. This is likely to mean that the company will have increased profits.
However, the new website meant that fewer customers were buying products in stores, which led to several stores making a loss. The fall in sales in stores and the losses at some stores may have meant that profits didn't increase as much as they could have.

Closing the stores which were making a loss in 2015 meant that Topstitch would have increased profits, since they no longer had the expense of the loss-making stores. However, some customers may not want to buy the products online. Since there are fewer high street stores, this may mean that the company will lose some customers, which may reduce profits in the future.
The catalogue of Topstitch is online rather than printed on paper, which will save the firm money in printing costs. They will also save money on postage, since they no longer have to post the catalogues out to customers. This reduction in costs will have helped to increase profits.

Page 66 — Sources of Finance — Small Firms

1 C ***[1 mark]***

2 Trade credit: e.g. if the business makes the payment too late, it could have to pay a large fee ***[1 mark]***.
A loan from a friend: e.g. the friend may expect to get a share in the profits of the business ***[1 mark]***.
A government grant: e.g. there are fewer options available / there may be strict criteria that a firm has to meet to get the grant / the firm may be limited to spending the money in a specific way ***[1 mark]***.

3.1 A business pays a deposit on the item they want to buy ***[1 mark]*** and then pays the rest of the cost of the item in installments over a period of time ***[1 mark]*** while they have use of the item ***[1 mark]***.

3.2 E.g. it may take a long time to raise enough money to buy the equipment outright ***[1 mark]***. Using the hire purchase scheme, he only needs to pay a deposit to begin with ***[1 mark]***, so he may be able to buy the equipment sooner ***[1 mark]***.

Page 67 — Sources of Finance — Established Firms

Warm-Up
External: new share issues, overdrafts, government grants, trade credit
Internal: retained profits, business savings

1 C ***[1 mark]***

2 E.g. there is a limit to how many assets a business can sell ***[1 mark]***. If the business sells too many assets, they won't be able to go on trading ***[1 mark]***.

3.1 E.g. issuing new shares will generate a large amount of money — much more than is needed to buy the computers ***[1 mark]***. Issuing shares means that the existing owners would lose some control over their business ***[1 mark]***. It wouldn't be worth losing this control for the benefit of buying the computers ***[1 mark]***.

3.2 Hint — there are two marks here, so make sure that you give one source of finance and one reason why it would be an appropriate way of financing the computers.
E.g. retained profits ***[1 mark]***, as these would not have the same costs associated with them as with external sources of finance / would not result in a loss of control over the business ***[1 mark]***.

Page 68 — Investments

1.1 E.g. new buildings ***[1 mark]*** and more employees ***[1 mark]***.

1.2 total profit of investment = 17 000 + 13 000 + 15 000 + 15 000 + 12 000 – 20 000 = £52 000
average annual profit = 52 000 ÷ 5 = £10 400
average rate of return = (average annual profit ÷ initial investment) × 100
average rate of return = (10 400 ÷ 20 000) × 100 = **52%**
[4 marks for correct answer, otherwise 1 mark for correct total profit of investment, 1 mark for correct average annual profit and 1 mark for using the correct equation to calculate the average rate of return]

1.3 The average rate of return on the investment is quite large ***[1 mark]***. This means Speedy Wheels should quickly see its profits increase as a result of the investment ***[1 mark]***. So Speedy Wheels is likely to go ahead with its decision to invest in the new delivery vans ***[1 mark]***.

Pages 69-70 — Break-Even Analysis

1 A ***[1 mark]***

2.1 Year 2: 450 × 7 = £3150 ***[1 mark]***
Year 3: 1200 × 7 = £8400 ***[1 mark]***

2.2 Year 2 ***[1 mark]***, since in this year the total money received was less than the total costs ***[1 mark]***.

3 E.g. fixed costs are costs that don't change with output ***[1 mark]***, for example, the cost of renting a building ***[1 mark]***. Variable costs are costs that increase as output increases ***[1 mark]***, for example, the cost of raw materials for making a product ***[1 mark]***.

4.1 Break-even output is the level of output where the company just covers its costs ***[1 mark]***. For example, the break-even output in Figure 2 is 500 units ***[1 mark]***, since this is the point where the revenue is equal to total costs ***[1 mark]***.

4.2 break-even output = 500 units ***[1 mark]***
margin of safety = 800 – 500 = 300 units ***[1 mark]***

4.3 How to grade your answer:
Level 0: Nothing written worthy of credit. ***[No marks]***
Level 1: Some attempt to describe how a break-even analysis could be useful to Ryan in getting a loan, but with little analysis of how it could be useful. ***[1 to 2 marks]***
Level 2: A number of ways a break-even analysis could be useful for Ryan in getting a loan have been described, with some analysis of how it could be useful. ***[3 to 4 marks]***
Level 3: There is a detailed description of the ways in which a break-even analysis could be useful for Ryan in getting a loan, and a clear analysis of how it could be useful. ***[5 to 6 marks]***
Here are some points your answer may include:
Ryan will be able to show that his predicted income for his first six months has a reasonably large margin of safety. A large margin of safety will mean that it's likely that he'll be able to pay back the interest on his loan.
He will also be able to show that his variable costs rise at a lower rate than his revenue. So as his output increases he should find it easier to cover his costs and therefore have enough money to make repayments on his loan.
This means that the bank will be more likely to invest in his business because his predictions suggest that it isn't likely that the business will lose the bank's money.

Pages 71-72 — Cash Flow

Warm-Up

inflow, selling, outflow, paying, net, positive

1 E.g. at certain times throughout the year, a company may be paying out more money than it is taking in ***[1 mark]***. But if the company earns more than it spends overall during the year, it will make a profit ***[1 mark]***.

2.1 E.g. businesses can use cash flow forecasts to predict whether they will have difficulties making payments in the future ***[1 mark]***, which means they can arrange additional finance if necessary for certain periods ***[1 mark]***.

2.2 Tele-wheels would need additional finance for June and July ***[1 mark]***, because it has a negative bank balance at the beginning or end of these months ***[1 mark]***.

3.1 August cash inflow = 1400 ***[1 mark]***

To find this value, you have to look at the orders made in June, These orders will be paid for after the 2 months of credit has passed.

July cash outflow = 1350 ***[1 mark]***

The net cash flow is –50. So the cash outflow must be £50 more than the cash inflow, which is 1300 + 50 = 1350.

June opening balance = –250 or (250) ***[1 mark]***

The opening balance for June will be the closing balance for May.

May net cash flow = –850 or (850) ***[1 mark]***

The net cash flow is the cash inflow minus the cash outflow, which is 350 – 1200 = –850.

October closing balance = 1850 ***[1 mark]***

To calculate the closing balance, just add up the net cash flow and the opening balance: 1100 + 750 = 1850.

3.2 The opening balance is the business's bank balance at the start of the month ***[1 mark]***; the closing balance is its bank balance at the end of the month ***[1 mark]***.

3.3 How to grade your answer:

Level 0: Nothing worthy of credit. ***[No marks]***

Level 1: Some attempt to describe the way in which the rise in demand may affect Yoo Too Sunglasses Ltd.'s cash flow but with little analysis of the consequences of these effects. ***[1 to 2 marks]***

Level 2: A number of ways in which the rise in demand may affect Yoo Too Sunglasses Ltd.'s cash flow have been described, with some analysis of what impact these effects might have. ***[3 to 4 marks]***

Level 3: There is a detailed description of the ways in which the rise in demand may affect Yoo Too Sunglasses Ltd.'s cash flow, and a clear analysis of the impacts these effects might have on the business. ***[5 to 6 marks]***

Here are some points your answer may include:

The increase in demand is likely to mean that it is advantageous for Yoo Too Sunglasses Ltd. to manufacture more sunglasses than they otherwise would have done in November.

The cash outflow for Yoo Too Sunglasses Ltd. in November might increase as the business spends more money on manufacturing more sunglasses.

This might mean that Yoo Too Sunglasses Ltd. will have to take out short-term finance to cover their costs during this period.

The cash inflow is likely to increase in the following January as the credit from customers who have bought sunglasses is paid off.

This may mean that Yoo Too Sunglasses Ltd. will find it easier to pay off their bills during this period.

As Yoo Too Sunglasses Ltd. will have extra cash in the business, they may choose to make investments into the business in January. This might improve the business's cash flow in the future.

Page 73 — Cash Flow — Problems

1 Hint — there are lots of options you can choose from, but for full marks you need to remember to explain each one. E.g. poor cash flow may mean that staff are not paid on time ***[1 mark]***, which could cause resentment and poor motivation amongst staff ***[1 mark]***. The business may not be able to pay invoices on time ***[1 mark]***, which may mean it loses out on discounts suppliers offer for paying promptly ***[1 mark]***. Creditors may not get paid on time ***[1 mark]***, which could cause them to insist on stricter credit terms in the future/take legal action to recover the debt ***[1 mark]***.

2.1 E.g. The credit period that Shoesies Ltd. gives its customers is longer than the credit period it has to pay its suppliers ***[1 mark]***. This means it has to pay out money for its supplies before money has come in from sales, which is a problem ***[1 mark]***. Recently, sales have been decreasing ***[1 mark]***, which could be a problem as cash inflow may be going down, while it's unlikely that cash outflow will have changed as much ***[1 mark]***.

2.2 How to grade your answer:

Level 0: Nothing written worthy of credit. ***[No marks]***

Level 1: Some attempt to recommend which option Shoesies Ltd. should take, but with little explanation for why this should be done. ***[1 to 3 marks]***

Level 2: Some of the advantages and disadvantages of the different options have been described, along with a recommendation of what Shoesies Ltd. should do. There is some reasoning to the recommendation, but it is lacking in detail or not fully explained. ***[4 to 6 marks]***

Level 3: There is a thorough description of the advantages and disadvantages of the different options, with a detailed recommendation for what Shoesies Ltd. should do that has been fully explained. ***[7 to 9 marks]***

Here are some points your answer may include:

Rescheduling payments:

Shoesies Ltd. could reschedule their credit agreements so that the credit period for their customers is shorter than the credit period for their suppliers.

They could also reschedule their loan repayments with their bank, so that they take place when there is enough cash in the business.

This would mean that their cash inflow would come in before their cash outflow.

However, they may find it hard to reschedule payments with suppliers and they may find that they attract fewer customers with a less generous credit agreement.

Obtaining another source of finance:

They could also look for new investors to increase the amount of cash in the business. This would be a good way of getting a large amount of cash relatively quickly, but would mean that the owners of the company would get less of their profits.

The owners of Shoesies Ltd. could ask for a loan from a friend or family member. This would help with the business's immediate cash flow problems but the loan would eventually need to be repaid. Therefore, the business would not be able to rely on loans in order to completely solve the cash flow problem.

They could arrange an overdraft with their bank for times in which they know they will run out of cash. This would be a good way of ensuring that they can keep up with payments to suppliers, but overdrafts are also expensive and would eventually have to be paid back.
As sales are decreasing, Shoesies Ltd. may find it difficult to get the cash needed to pay back a loan or overdraft. Shoesies Ltd. is already unable to make its loan repayments, so obtaining another loan from its bank would probably drive it further into debt.

Make sure you finish your answer with a conclusion recommending what you think Shoesies Ltd. should do — it doesn't matter which you choose as long as you give reasons. E.g. 'Shoesies Ltd. should reschedule their payments. Although this may be difficult, it would be a longer-term solution than obtaining a new source of finance and would also be less expensive.'

Pages 74-75 — Income Statements

Warm-Up
cost of sales — the amount of money needed to make products.
gross profit — the amount of money left over from the revenue after direct costs are taken into account.
operating profit — the amount of money left over from the revenue after all direct and indirect costs are taken into account.

1 B ***[1 mark]***

2.1 Any two from: e.g. wages/salaries / rent/rates / office expenses / advertising / depreciation ***[2 marks — 1 mark for each correct answer]***

2.2 Change in profits = 319m – 287.6m = 31.4m
Percentage change = (31.4 ÷ 287.6) × 100 = **10.9%**
[2 marks for correct answer, otherwise 1 mark for correctly calculating change in profits]

3.1 E.g. if the operating profit is significantly lower than the gross profit ***[1 mark]***, then this suggests that the company spends too much on indirect costs ***[1 mark]*** and therefore may be risky for investors to invest in ***[1 mark]***.

3.2 How to grade your answer:
Level 0: Nothing worthy of credit. ***[No marks]***
Level 1: There is some attempt to state the effects of these actions on Williams' Construction Ltd., but there is little or no explanation of why these effects happened. ***[1 to 2 marks]***
Level 2: There is a basic analysis of how these actions will affect Williams' Construction Ltd., but the explanations are lacking in detail, or points have been missed. ***[3 to 4 marks]***
Level 3: There is a thorough analysis of how these actions will affect Williams' Construction Ltd., with detailed explanations of the causes of these effects. ***[5 to 6 marks]***
Here are some points your answer may include:
Making staff redundant reduced the cost of wages and salaries from £90m to £65m.
Closing offices reduced the rent and rates expenses of the company from £65m to £45m.
It also reduced office expenses from £30m to £20m.
These actions may also have contributed to the drop in other expenses from £31m to £24m.
This drop in expenses meant that operating profit was higher in 2017 compared to 2016, despite the fact that gross profit was lower than in 2016.
This meant that net profit and retained profit were higher in 2017 than in 2016.

Page 76 — Profit Margins

1 The business spends little money making the products that it sells ***[1 mark]***, but it spends a lot of money on indirect costs, such as salaries and rent ***[1 mark]***.

2.1 gross profit margin = (gross profit ÷ sales revenue) × 100
= (690 000 ÷ 3 000 000) × 100 = **23%**
[2 marks for correct answer, otherwise 1 mark for using the correct equation]

2.2 net profit = gross profit – (other operating expenses and interest)
= 690 000 – 510 000 = 180 000
net profit margin = (net profit ÷ sales revenue) × 100
= (180 000 ÷ 3 000 000) × 100 = **6%**
[3 marks for correct answer, otherwise 1 mark for calculating net profit, 1 mark for using the correct equation to calculate net profit margin]

2.3 The business has a relatively low net profit margin compared to its gross profit margin ***[1 mark]***. Reducing the amount the business spends on insurance would help to increase its net profit margin ***[1 mark]***.

3 The amount of money being spent on each product by customers will increase ***[1 mark]***, but the cost of making each product will stay the same ***[1 mark]***. Therefore a smaller percentage of the money spent by customers will go towards making the product ***[1 mark]***, resulting in a higher gross profit margin ***[1 mark]***.

Pages 77-78 — Statements of Financial Position

1 B ***[1 mark]***

2 D ***[1 mark]***

3 Current liabilities are payments that must be made within one year of the date of the balance sheet ***[1 mark]***, for example unpaid corporation tax / creditors ***[1 mark]***. Long-term liabilities are debts that the company has more than one year to repay ***[1 mark]***, for example, bank loans ***[1 mark]***.

You might have used different examples in your answer, but as long as they're correct, you'll still get the marks.

4.1 Share capital is money that was put into a business when shares were originally issued ***[1 mark]***. A firm can raise finance by issuing new shares ***[1 mark]***.

4.2 Retained profits are profits that are put back into a business ***[1 mark]***, and can be used to finance future investments ***[1 mark]***.

5 Capital employed is the total money that the business has received ***[1 mark]***. The net assets is the amount the business would make if it sold all its assets (in theory) ***[1 mark]***. The value of the firm's net assets must be the same as the capital employed because the capital employed accounts for all the money used to purchase the net assets ***[1 mark]***.

6.1 Assets are valuable items owned by the business, or money owed to the business ***[1 mark]***. For example, the machinery that J. Logan owned in November 2016 was an asset ***[1 mark]***. Liabilities are money that is owed to others ***[1 mark]***. For example, J. Logan had £200 of liabilities in November 2016 as it owed money to its creditors ***[1 mark]***.

6.2 total finance used = 2500 + 3500 + 1000 = £7000
% which is share capital = (2500 ÷ 7000) × 100 = **35.7%**
[2 marks for correct answer, otherwise 1 mark for correctly calculating total finance]

Page 79 — Analysis — Statements of Financial Position

Warm-Up

stakeholders, capital, liabilities

1 D ***[1 mark]***

A company's fixed assets are things that it keeps long-term, e.g. buildings, machinery etc. So the only option given here that would reduce a company's fixed assets is D, since it involves selling property.

2 How to grade your answer:

Level 0: Nothing worthy of credit. ***[No marks]***

Level 1: There is some description of how investing cash in new machinery may affect the financial performance of the business. ***[1 to 2 marks]***

Level 2: There is an analysis of how investing cash in new machinery may affect the financial performance of the business. Factors on the statement of financial position that existing shareholders will be interested in have been described. ***[3 to 4 marks]***

Level 3: There is a detailed analysis of the factors on the statement of financial position that existing shareholders will be interested in and how they will be affected by investing cash in new machinery. ***[5 to 6 marks]***

Here are some points your answer may include:

Investing cash in new machinery will increase the value of fixed assets and decrease the value of current assets.

Investing £3000 in new equipment means the business' current assets will be less than its current liabilities.

Shareholders may be concerned that the decrease in current assets may mean the company has difficulty paying off its current liabilities.

Existing shareholders may be interested in an increase in fixed assets as it could mean that the company will be able to provide more haircuts in the future.

This could lead to an increase in sales and an increase in profits.

An increase in profits will mean that shareholders should get a larger share dividend.

Page 80 — Analysis — Competitors

1.1 Competitors may work in different ways ***[1 mark]***, so it can be difficult to compare the same factors on the different financial statements ***[1 mark]***.

1.2 How to grade your answer:

Level 0: Nothing worthy of credit. ***[No marks]***

Level 1: There is some attempt to recommend what Lucia's should do, but with little explanation as to why this should be done. ***[1 to 3 marks]***

Level 2: Some of the advantages and disadvantages of increasing the bank loan have been given, along with a recommendation of what Lucia's should do. There is some reasoning to the recommendation, but it is lacking in detail or not fully explained. ***[4 to 6 marks]***

Level 3: There is a thorough description of the advantages and disadvantages of increasing the loan, with a detailed recommendation of what Lucia's should do that has been fully explained. ***[7 to 9 marks]***

Here are some points your answer may include:

Currently, Lucia's has much higher current liabilities than Pizza Roma. This means it's more at risk than Pizza Roma of having difficulties paying its creditors.

So it would improve Lucia's financial performance compared to Pizza Roma if it spends money on paying off these liabilities.

Taking out a loan would increase Lucia's liabilities, and they may have difficulty paying it off in the future.

Lucia's currently has £13 000 cash in hand.

Instead of taking out a loan, Lucia's could invest some of its cash in paying its creditors and overdraft. This would mean its overall liabilities would go down.

At the moment, Lucia's has invested in less machinery than Pizza Roma. This means Lucia's may not be able to produce as much pizza as Pizza Roma.

Lucia's could invest in machinery rather than paying off its current liabilities.

Having more machinery will mean that Lucia's will be able to make and sell more pizza. This may mean that Lucia's revenue and profits will increase.

So its retained profits could also increase, improving its financial performance compared to Pizza Roma.

Lucia's could then use the increased revenue to help them to pay off their current liabilities.

Make sure you finish your answer with a conclusion recommending what you think Lucia's should do — it doesn't matter which you choose as long as you give reasons. E.g. 'Lucia's shouldn't pay off its current liabilities straight away. Instead, it should invest some of its cash in machinery. This means their liabilities won't increase, but the machinery could help to increase their revenue, which in turn could help them pay their creditors and overdraft, and help to improve their financial performance compared to Pizza Roma.

Pages 81-88 — Mixed Questions

1 A ***[1 mark]***

2 A ***[1 mark]***

3 C ***[1 mark]***

The caravan retailer sells 45 caravans each month and sells each one for £20 000. Revenue = sales × price = 45 × 20 000 = £900 000.

4 total revenue = 15 000 + 17 500 + 16 800 + 19 300 + 21 250 = £89 850

average revenue = 89850 ÷ 5 = **£17 970** ***[2 marks for correct answer, otherwise 1 mark for correctly calculating total revenue]***

5 Any two from: e.g. expanding via e-commerce / opening new stores / outsourcing / franchising ***[2 marks — 1 mark for each correct answer]***

6 Using unwanted assets as a source of finance means selling things that the business owns that are no longer in use ***[1 mark]***. This source of finance would be more suited to established businesses ***[1 mark]***, as they are more likely to have assets that they have stopped using ***[1 mark]***.

7 E.g. staff on zero hour contracts don't have any contracted hours ***[1 mark]***. This means that staff don't have to accept any hours that are offered to them ***[1 mark]***, so firms might find themselves short of labour at times ***[1 mark]***.

8 A just-in-time method of production means that once raw materials have been delivered, they are quickly made into products and delivered to customers ***[1 mark]***. This saves the business money as it means they don't have to store much/any stock ***[1 mark]***.

9 E.g. under the Equality Act 2010, all of a firm's employees must be paid the same if they do the same job or work of equal value ***[1 mark]***. This may mean that a firm has to pay some of its staff more than it would do without the legislation ***[1 mark]***. The Equality Act 2010 also means that a firm can be held responsible if any of its employees discriminate against another person ***[1 mark]***. This may mean that a firm has to spend money on staff training / writing policies about equal rights ***[1 mark]***.

10.1 A sole trader business is owned by just one person ***[1 mark]***, whereas a partnership has at least two and generally up to twenty partners who own the business ***[1 mark]***.

10.2 Any two from: e.g. government grant / overdraft / mortgage / trade credit ***[2 marks — 1 mark for each correct answer]***

10.3 Hint: labour supply, competition, location of the market and cost are all likely to influence their decision on where to locate. It doesn't matter which of these factors you choose as long as you explain why they would matter specifically to Mel and Paul.
E.g. the location of the market would influence their decision on where to locate ***[1 mark]*** as they would want to be somewhere that customers could easily get to ***[1 mark]***. Competition may influence their decision ***[1 mark]*** as they may want to locate somewhere away from the competition so they don't lose customers ***[1 mark]***.

10.4 How to grade your answer:
Level 0: Nothing worthy of credit. ***[No marks]***
Level 1: Some attempt to describe the suitability of the promotional methods, but there is little or no explanation to back up these descriptions. ***[1 to 2 marks]***
Level 2: There is a basic analysis of the suitability of the promotional methods for Cut of the Action, but the explanations are lacking in detail, or points have been missed. ***[3 to 4 marks]***
Level 3: There is a thorough analysis of the suitability of the promotional methods for Cut of the Action, with detailed explanations of to back up these conclusions. ***[5 to 6 marks]***
Here are some points your answer may include:
Local newspaper adverts would target people specifically in the local area. This would be good for a hairdressing salon, as people generally want to use a hairdresser in their local area.
However, advertising in a newspaper may cost more than some other methods of promotion that would target a local audience, such as posters.
Also, the number of people reading newspapers is declining, so many people in their target market might not see the adverts.
Mel and Paul have also chosen to promote their business by sponsoring events at a local art college.
Mel and Paul are opening a 'modern' hairdressing salon, which suggests they are targeting a young market that may be interested in events at the art college. This means the sponsorship may help to get their name recognised by their target market.
However, the event they are sponsoring is only held once a year, so this method of promotion won't give their business regular exposure. People may not need to visit a hairdresser's while the exhibition is on, and may quickly forget the name of the salon once the exhibition is over. Also, if the art exhibition receives bad publicity, having their name associated with the event could damage the image of Mel and Paul's business.

11.1 Simpson's variable costs would have increased because output increased ***[1 mark]***, so they would need to spend more on things like raw materials and factory labour ***[1 mark]***.

11.2 E.g. social media offers customers a quick and easy way to get in touch with Simpson's ***[1 mark]***, so it means any queries they have can be answered quickly ***[1 mark]***.

11.3 The introduction of the National Living Wage meant that Simpson's had to pay all workers aged 25 or over more than they were legally required to before ***[1 mark]***. This may have led to an increase in Simpson's wage bill ***[1 mark]***, meaning it decided to increase prices to minimise the effect of these increased costs on its profits ***[1 mark]***.

11.4 How to grade your answer:
Level 0: Nothing worthy of credit. ***[No marks]***
Level 1: There is some attempt to state how introducing the new environmental policy might affect the shareholders of Simpson's Soap Plc, but there is little or no explanation of why these effects might happen. ***[1 to 2 marks]***
Level 2: There is a basic analysis of how introducing the new environmental policy might affect the shareholders of Simpson's Soap Plc, but the explanations are lacking in detail, or points have been missed. ***[3 to 4 marks]***
Level 3: There is a thorough analysis of how introducing the new environmental policy might affect the shareholders of Simpson's Soap Plc, with detailed explanations of the causes of these effects. ***[5 to 6 marks]***
Here are some points your answer may include:
The new environmental policy may please many of its shareholders as customers are becoming more aware of how businesses affect the environment. This means that many customers are choosing to buy products from businesses that try to minimise their negative impact on the environment and use sustainable resources. The new environmental policy may make Simpson's more popular than its competitors, leading to an increase in sales and possibly a greater increase in profit in the future. More profit means that the shareholders could get more dividends.
However, adhering to the new environmental policy is likely to be expensive, and Simpson's thinks it has already negatively affected its profits. The environmental policy may not lead to a big increase in sales, meaning that, in financial terms, the benefits of having the environmental policy may not outweigh the costs.
This could mean that profits are reduced, and so shareholders could get smaller dividends.

12.1 2007 net profit margin = (net profit ÷ revenue) × 100
= (164 000 ÷ 800 000) × 100 = 20.5%
difference in profit margins = 20.5 – 18.2 = **2.3%**
[3 marks for correct answer, otherwise 1 mark for using the correct equation to calculate net profit margin, 1 mark for correct calculation of 2007 net profit margin]

12.2 Sales of gardening products at the supermarket increased from 4% of total non-food sales in 2005 to 9% in 2007 ***[1 mark]***. This suggests that demand from the supermarket's customers for gardening products has increased ***[1 mark]***, so the SpadeAce may sell better there in 2008 than it would have in 2005 ***[1 mark]***.

12.3 E.g. telesales would have been very time-consuming for Diggitup Ltd. ***[1 mark]*** as they would have had to spend lots of time packaging and distributing small orders ***[1 mark]***.

12.4 The SpadeAce is likely to have been called a star *[1 mark]*, as the rapid increase in demand suggests it had high market growth *[1 mark]* and the fact that it was voted the most popular product for piece of gardening equipment by professional gardeners suggests it has high market share *[1 mark]*.

12.5 Hint: there are lots of possible answers here. Make sure that you fully explain whatever two reasons you give.
E.g. Diggitup Ltd. may have had to spend money on researching the market *[1 mark]* so that they remained aware of any new competitor products on the market *[1 mark]*. Diggitup Ltd. may also have had to spend more money on promotion *[1 mark]* to persuade customers to continue buying their products rather than switching to new competitors' products *[1 mark]*.

12.6 How to grade your answer:
Level 0: Nothing worthy of credit. *[No marks]*
Level 1: The student has stated some impacts of the changing economic climate on Diggitup Ltd., but with little explanation of why these could happen. *[1 to 3 marks]*
Level 2: The student has given a basic explanation of some of the impacts that the changing economic climate would be likely to have on Diggitup Ltd. There is some attempt to conclude which area will have the biggest impact on the company's plans for growth, but with little or no explanation to justify the conclusion. *[4 to 6 marks]*
Level 3: The student has explained the impacts that the changing economic climate would be likely to have on Diggitup Ltd. There is a conclusion as to which area will have the biggest impact on the company's plans for growth, but the justification is lacking in detail. *[7 to 9 marks]*
Level 4: There is a detailed and thorough analysis of how changes to the economic climate would have been likely to affect Diggitup Ltd. A conclusion has been made as to which area will have the biggest impact on the company's plans for growth, which has been fully justified using evidence. *[10 to 12 marks]*
Here are some points your answer may include:
<u>Impacts on consumer spending</u>
A high unemployment rate means more people are out of work, so many people have less money available to spend.
The unemployment rate increased from 5.2% to 7.8% between the start of 2008 and the end of 2009. So consumer spending would have gone down.
The SpadeAce is a product that is a want, so it is likely demand for it may have fallen as unemployment rates rose.
A low interest rate means that it is cheaper to borrow money, and less interest is paid on money saved in the bank. This can cause people to spend more and save less.
The Bank of England base rate for interest decreased from 5.5% to 0.5% between the start of 2008 and the end of 2009. This means that most other interest rates are also likely to have fallen sharply within this time period.
The low interest rates may have meant that consumers would have been more likely to borrow money and less likely to save money. This means that consumer spending may have increased, which could have caused Diggitup Ltd.'s sales to increase.
<u>Impacts on business costs</u>
The falling interest rates would have meant that Diggitup Ltd. paid less in interest repayments on their loan. This fall in business costs would have meant they had more money available to invest in the business.
The value of the British pound fell by 3.4 against the yuan between the start of 2008 and the end of 2009.
This would have meant that it became more expensive for Diggitup Ltd. to import its raw materials. This would have left them with less money to invest in the business.
They could have increased their prices to cover the extra costs, but that may have led to a decline in sales, which would have made it more difficult for them to grow the business.

Make sure you finish your answer with a conclusion about whether changes to consumer spending or the business's costs will have the biggest impact on Diggitup Ltd.'s plans for growth — it doesn't matter which you choose as long as you give reasons. E.g. 'Although falling interest rates may have reduced some of Diggitup Ltd.'s costs, rising unemployment rates are likely to have reduced consumer spending, meaning that demand for Diggitup Ltd.'s products would have fallen. This fall in consumer spending is likely to have had the greatest impact on the company's growth plans.'

13.1 induction training *[1 mark]*, off-the-job training *[1 mark]*

13.2 The factory work is likely to involve the new employees learning how to do repetitive practical tasks such as operating machinery *[1 mark]*. On-the-job training would be appropriate as they could easily be shown these practical tasks by existing factory workers *[1 mark]*, and then be given a chance to practise them *[1 mark]*.

13.3 In flow production, products are made continuously on a production line *[1 mark]*. This is appropriate for Raymer's Ltd. as they are a baked-bean manufacturer so the products are likely to be identical / able to be mass produced *[1 mark]*.

13.4 E.g. the expansion is likely to mean that the firm will increase its output *[1 mark]*. This will create more work for the employees so they will benefit from job security *[1 mark]*. With an increased output, Raymer's Ltd. will need more raw materials, which will mean more income for their suppliers *[1 mark]*.

13.5 E.g. they could introduce a scheme such as total quality management *[1 mark]*, which would mean all employees are constantly focusing on quality *[1 mark]*.

13.6 E.g. Raymer's Ltd. are planning to expand by buying a new factory, so they might start taking on many more orders *[1 mark]*. Workers may be overwhelmed by the increase in volume and cut corners to make products quicker *[1 mark]*. Raymer's Ltd. estimate that they will need to increase their workforce by 15% and these new staff members will need training *[1 mark]*. Quality may suffer until the new staff are fully trained *[1 mark]*.

13.7 How to grade your answer:
Level 0: Nothing worthy of credit. *[No marks]*
Level 1: Some attempt has been made to recommend what Raymer's Ltd. should do, but with little explanation for why this should be done. *[1 to 3 marks]*
Level 2: Some of the advantages and disadvantages of internal and external recruitment have been given, along with a recommendation of what Raymer's Ltd. should do. There is some reasoning to the recommendation, but it is lacking in detail or not fully explained. *[4 to 6 marks]*

Level 3: There is a thorough description of the advantages and disadvantages of internal and external recruitment, with a detailed and fully explained recommendation of what Raymer's Ltd. should do. ***[7 to 9 marks]***

Here are some points your answer may include:

Internal recruitment

Promoting and training existing staff would boost staff motivation. This is likely to make staff more productive as they will want the business to do well and so do their jobs as best they can to help that to happen. Increased productivity could lead to increased profits for the firm.
More motivated staff are also more likely to stay with the firm. This could reduce Raymer's Ltd.'s recruitment and training costs in the future.
Recruiting internally would mean that Raymer's Ltd. saved money on advertising the job externally.
It would also mean that the new supervisors already knew a lot about the company, so they may need less training than an external recruit.
It also means that managers would know the candidate already, so they would have an idea of how suitable they were for the supervisor role. This may save time and money recruiting an external candidate and then later finding out that they were not right for the job.
Recruiting internally would mean that Raymer's Ltd. had to recruit new factory workers to replace those that had been promoted to supervisor, but they would need to recruit new factory workers anyway as part of the expansion, so this is unlikely to be a big problem.

External recruitment

Another local food manufacturing company has recently gone bust, so it's likely that there will be unemployed people in the area with supervisor experience. These people might require less training than some of the existing factory workers.
Recruiting externally would also mean that the new staff may be able to share some of their ideas and experiences from other jobs and introduce more productive ways of working.
It's likely that recruiting externally would give the firm more candidates to choose from, so they would have more chance of finding someone that is well suited to the role.
However, recruiting externally may take more time than recruiting internally. This might be a problem if the firm wants to expand quickly and needs to find staff as quickly as possible.

Make sure you finish your answer with a conclusion recommending what you think Raymer's Ltd. should do — it doesn't matter which you choose as long as you give reasons. E.g. "Raymer's Ltd. should fill the new supervisor positions by promoting existing factory workers. This will make staff feel more motivated, which may make them more productive and more likely to stay with the firm."

13.8 How to grade your answer:

Level 0: Nothing worthy of credit. ***[No marks]***

Level 1: The student has stated some likely impacts that the expansion would have had on the reputation of the business, but with little explanation of why these would happen. ***[1 to 3 marks]***

Level 2: The student has given a basic explanation of the likely impacts that the expansion would have had on the reputation of the business. There is some attempt to conclude which area will have the biggest impact on the business's reputation, but with little or no explanation to justify the conclusion. ***[4 to 6 marks]***

Level 3: The student has explained the likely impacts that the expansion would have had on the reputation of the business. There is a conclusion as to which area will have the biggest impact on the business's reputation, but the justification is lacking in detail. ***[7 to 9 marks]***

Level 4: There is a detailed and thorough analysis of the likely impacts that the expansion would have had on the reputation of the business. A conclusion has been made as to which area will have the biggest impact on the business's reputation, which has been fully justified using evidence. ***[10 to 12 marks]***

Here are some points your answer may include:

Customer service

The expansion meant that Raymer's Ltd. were able to take on some new customers. They agreed to use different labels for the supermarket's orders. Satisfying the customer's individual needs like this shows that Raymer's Ltd. were prepared to offer their customers a high level of customer service. This is likely to have improved the reputation of the business.
Raymer's Ltd. employed two customer service assistants. Having specific staff to deal with customer queries is likely to have improved customer service, as the staff are likely to have been trained so they had good product knowledge and knew how to resolve issues efficiently. This is likely to have made customers happy and improved the reputation of the business.
The percentage of products that were returned increased after the expansion. Supplying customers with poor quality products is a sign of poor customer service and is likely to have harmed the reputation of the business.

Consumer law

Consumer law states that a product must match its description and must be of satisfactory quality.
Following the expansion Raymer's Ltd. had a problem with products being returned because they contained a lower weight of produce than was stated on the label. This is breaking consumer law. They also had more products returned because of loose labels and dented tins. These factors mean that the products weren't of satisfactory quality, which again is breaking consumer law. Regularly breaking consumer law would have damaged the reputation of the business.

Make sure you finish your answer with a conclusion about whether the expansion's impact on customer service or on consumer law will have had the biggest impact on the reputation of the business — it doesn't matter which you choose as long as you give reasons. E.g. 'Although the expansion led to quality issues and situations where Raymer's Ltd. broke consumer law, the expansion meant that Raymer's Ltd. improved their customer service by employing extra customer service staff to specifically deal with customer queries. Even when customers did experience quality issues, the customer service staff may have ensured that problems were dealt with promptly, which would have had a positive effect on the reputation of the business.'

BUAQ41